$1.25

JOHN R. PIERCE
electrons
and waves

an introduction to the science of electronics and communication

A DOUBLEDAY ANCHOR BOOK

ELECTRONS AND WAVES

In this book, which is published as the first of two volumes in the Science Study Series, John R. Pierce has revised and extended the material on electronics and electromagnetism that he wrote for the general reading public in *Electrons, Waves and Messages* (Hanover House, 1956). When the earlier work appeared, many of today's technological marvels still were in the planning stage (including Telstar, in the development of which Dr. Pierce himself played a conspicuous part), and this new edition brings the topics up to date—if the onrush of science can be said to allow of so restricting a process as dating.

The author, who through most of his productive career has been associated with the Bell Laboratories, was at this writing the Visiting Distinguished Professor of Engineering Physics at the Desert Research Institute, of the University of Nevada. President Johnson, soon after taking office, cited Dr. Pierce for "outstanding contributions to communications theory, electron optics, and traveling wave tubes, and for analysis leading to world-wide radio communications using artificial earth satellites," and awarded him a 1963 National Medal of Science.

John R. Pierce was born on March 27, 1910, at Des Moines, Iowa. His first intellectual interest was mathematics, especially geometry, and boyhood tinkering with radio gave him a subsequently useful familiarity with electrical circuitry and vacuum tubes.

At the California Institute of Technology (where he received his B.S. in 1933, M.S. in 1934, and Ph.D. in 1936) he built and flew gliders, a heady experience that turned him toward aeronautical engineering. He wearied of drawing rivets, however, and decided that its lack of concern with rivets would make electrical engineering a profession more to his taste.

Pierce joined Bell Labs after receiving his Ph.D. and eventually became its Executive Director, Research-Communications Principles and Systems Divisions, with responsibility for such varied fields of research as radio, electronics, acoustics and vision, mathematics, computation, and psychology. He holds eighty-three patents for inventions in tubes and circuits, especially electron multipliers, electron guns, and microwave tubes. In 1954 he made an analysis of the possibility of radio relaying by satellite, and this analysis, with subsequent work along the same line, led to the 1960 launching of Project Echo, the forerunner of Telstar.

Pierce credits the science fiction of Jules Verne, H. G. Wells, and Hugo Gernsback with having excited his interest in science, and he himself has composed in the genre, under the nom de plume "J. J. Coupling." His serious writing includes, besides *Electrons, Waves and Messages*: *Theory and Design of Electric Beams* (Van Nostrand, 1949); *Traveling Wave Tubes* (Van Nostrand, 1950); *Man's World of Sound*, in collaboration with Edward E. David, Jr. (Doubleday, 1958); *Waves and the Ear*, in collaboration with Willem A. van Bergeijk and Edward E. David, Jr. (Science Study Series, 1960); *Symbols, Signals and Noise* (Harper & Row, 1961), and many articles in general magazines and technical journals.

He has received the following awards: Eta Kappa Nu, 1942; Morris Liebmann Memorial Prize, 1947; Stuart Ballantine Medal, 1960; Air Force Association H. H. Arnold Trophy, 1962; the Golden Plate Award of the Academy of Achievement, 1962; the Arnold Air Society General Hoyt S. Vandenberg Trophy, 1963; and the following honorary degrees: D.Eng. from the Newark College of Engineering, 1961; D.Sc. from Northwestern University, 1961; D.Sc. from Yale University, 1963; D.Sc. from Polytechnic Institute of Brooklyn, 1963.

Dr. Pierce is a member of the National Academy of Sciences and the Air Force Association, and a Fellow of the American Academy of Arts and Sciences, the Institute of Electrical and Electronics Engineers, the American Physical Society, the Acoustical Society of America, the American Astronautical Society, and the British Interplanetary Society. He is a Kentucky colonel.

Electrons and Waves

BY

JOHN R. PIERCE

This book is a revised and enlarged edition of the
first eight chapters of *Electrons, Waves and Messages*
which was published in 1956 by Doubleday & Company, Inc.

Published by Anchor Books
Doubleday & Company, Inc.
Garden City, New York

Illustrations by Felix Cooper

Library of Congress Catalog Card Number 64–25265

THE SCIENCE STUDY SERIES

The Science Study Series offers to students and to the general public the writing of distinguished authors on the most stirring and fundamental topics of science, from the smallest known particles to the whole universe. Some of the books tell of the role of science in the world of man, his technology and civilization. Others are biographical in nature, telling the fascinating stories of the great discoverers and their discoveries. All the authors have been selected both for expertness in the fields they discuss and for ability to communicate their special knowledge and their own views in an interesting way. The primary purpose of these books is to provide a survey within the grasp of the young student or the layman. Many of the books, it is hoped, will encourage the reader to make his own investigations of natural phenomena.

The Series, which now offers topics in all the sciences and their applications, had its beginning in a project to revise the secondary schools' physics curriculum. At the Massachusetts Institute of Technology during 1956 a group of physicists, high school teachers, journalists, apparatus designers, film producers, and other specialists organized the Physical Science Study Committee, now operating as a part of Educational Services Incorporated, Watertown,

Massachusetts. They pooled their knowledge and experience toward the design and creation of aids to the learning of physics. Initially their effort was supported by the National Science Foundation, which has continued to aid the program. The Ford Foundation, the Fund for the Advancement of Education, and the Alfred P. Sloan Foundation have also given support. The Committee has created a text book, an extensive film series, a laboratory guide, especially designed apparatus, and a teacher's source book.

The Series is guided by a Board of Editors consisting of Bruce F. Kingsbury, Managing Editor; John H. Durston, General Editor; Paul F. Brandwein, the Conservation Foundation and Harcourt, Brace & World, Inc.; Samuel A. Goudsmit, Brookhaven National Laboratory; Philippe LeCorbeiller, Harvard University; and Gerard Piel, *Scientific American*.

PREFACE

This book follows very closely the first eight chapters of *Electrons, Waves and Messages* (Doubleday & Company, Inc., New York), which was published in 1956. The material has been brought up to date, and some of it has, I hope, been made clearer and put in better order.

The preface to the earlier volume contained acknowledgments which I will not repeat and reservations and explanations which seem to me superfluous. It has interested me in revising this material to see how little needed to be changed. Chiefly, a few topical examples have been included and some of the examples of devices pruned away as redundant.

In making revisions I owe a great deal to John H. Durston of Educational Services Incorporated, who pointed out passages that were difficult or unclear and material that was too detailed.

J. R. Pierce

CONTENTS

Telescopes and Microscopes. Microwave Transmission. Reflection and the Standing Wave. Trapped Waves. The Concept of Waves.

ELECTRONS AND WAVES

Chapter One

ELECTRONICS AND THE WORLD

When I used to commute to New York by train, I passed a surprising number of technical enterprises: a pump company, an electrical-instrument company, a computing-machine company, and a lot of others. Now, as I occasionally drive to the city, I see more: a company making furnace controls, a tractor company, a company making potentiometers, a host of companies engaged in various sorts of engineering or scientific work. This makes me feel very ignorant and humble. After seven years of undergraduate and graduate study, followed by twenty-eight years of research in an industrial laboratory, I know a good deal about a segment of one field, electronics. I have no detailed and expert knowledge about even most of the other work done in the company which employs me. Outside of that company, all sorts of things go on about which I have only the vaguest sort of information. With so much to know, is it not hopeless even for an expert to try to understand our science and technology? Is it not even more hopeless for an outsider to try to understand these matters? Should he try?

Literate and curious men of every age have thought and read and learned about matters outside of their immediate physical needs and experience. What they have thought and read and learned has varied from age to age, as both the tasks of everyday life and the aspirations that go beyond these tasks have changed. Sometimes men have been concerned with religion, sometimes with mathematics and philosophy, sometimes with exploration, trade and conquest, sometimes with the theory and practice of government, sometimes with ancient learning, sometimes with the arts.

In different times, in different cultures, these matters have engaged the attention of the unusually able and intelligent men. When some of the best thought and best effort of a culture is spent in political philosophy, or in classical learning, or in art, the cultured man is the man who is acquainted with, and whose thought reflects, political philosophy, or classical learning, or art.

The Age of Science and Technology

One can scarcely deny that the most effective thinking of our age, and a great deal of its energy and enterprise, go into science, and especially into the sort of science which guides an immensely complicated technology in doing new things and in doing old things cheaper and better. This prodigious technology in turn supports science with a lavishness unprecedented in any former age.

It is not only true that the world about us would astound a man of a much earlier age. It would astound a man of fifty years ago almost as much. He could not help being astounded by electric power, washing machines, dishwashers, freezers, highways, automobiles, radio, television, airplanes, rockets, satellites, spacecraft, nuclear energy. The widespread good living, the rarity of servants, the diminution of great luxury would astound him as much. If he looked more deeply, the growth of science—both in knowledge, in magnitude of effort, and in monetary reward and public recognition as well—would astound him.

The world of fifty years ago had writers, poets, painters, musicians, philosophers, politicians—and governments. No doubt all of these have changed of recent years. It is clear, however, that the great, the characteristic, the significant changes have been in science and technology and in the way the world is divided into countries and governed. We might even argue that the tremendous political upheavals of our age are primarily a consequence of a revolution in science and technology. Whether or not we go this far, it is clear that science and technology, together with political change and turmoil, are the outstanding features of our culture. Many would put science and technology first.

One cannot be in tune with the age without understanding something of science. This unmistakable truth is receiving increasing recognition in our educational system, although some men who profess to be educated flee frantically from the most significant feature of their culture and seek culture in almost any place but where it is to be found. It sometimes seems to me that writing, painting and music have become weak, ineffective and discouraged by shutting themselves off from the vigorous thought and achievement of the present. Yet, there could be great nourishment of the arts in both the understanding and insight afforded by science and in the tools provided by technology as well.

Suppose we do grant that our science and technology are the great and important contributions of our era, the first things that men should know about when they look beyond the tasks and problems of the day and want to partake in some measure of the spirit and achievement of the times. Is it not hopeless to try to understand a science and technology so multifarious that no scientist can grasp all the details of more than a tiny fraction of it? I believe the answer to be no.

In the past there was less technology to understand. However, in the past technology was empirical art. The understanding of those who had mastered its skills and rules did not go beyond those skills and rules themselves. It seems to me that the outstanding feature of modern technology is that skill, rule of thumb, art, are rapidly being replaced or explained by science, by understanding. Engineering education, which waxes brilliantly while much of education flourishes dubiously, is continually being freed from detailed art and special knowledge to make way for more physics and mathematics, for more and wider fundamental understanding. The engineers who are graduated today are far better educated than I was twenty-eight years ago. Their education is tougher, they learn more that is fundamental and broadly important, and they spend less time on special rules and tedious art. Engineering by handbook is not enough in the modern world. Handbooks last scarcely long enough to become familiar before they are outmoded. An engineer must understand and think to keep up with his art.

My specialty was for a long time vacuum tubes, and particularly microwave vacuum tubes. It is true that

I had special knowledge, but this alone did not suffice. I found that in contemplating new problems in old tubes, and new tubes themselves, I was continually led into considering related and analogous problems in other branches of science and technology.

When I studied the electromagnetic waves in a traveling-wave amplifier, I could easily go on and trace them out through the waveguide of a radar, to the antenna, and from the antenna into space, perhaps as far as a communication satellite and back again. Understanding these waves, I can understand the sound waves in the air, the waves in the ocean, and waves of light. I can understand how small an object a biologist can see through his microscope, and how fine detail an astronomer can hope to see on the planet Mars. Through understanding the motions of electrons in a vacuum tube, I can understand the motion of the planets in their orbits and the paths that satellites take through space.

No longer can any effective part of our science and technology be an island unto itself. Actual content overlaps the boundaries, and mathematical methods and physical concepts are shared widely. To know a part of science or technology well is to know something of the whole.

Thus, while I am astonished and dismayed at the total scope of the enterprises past which I ride or drive, I know that should I inquire concerning them I would find something familiar about them. I would find connected with them men who talk the language of science. The details of what they would say would be unfamiliar, but what they explained I could in some measure understand and appreciate.

The Popularization of Science

This appreciation of their activities makes me want to tell these colleagues of mine something about my particular field of work. I am sure that what I have to say will be clear and interesting to communication and electronics engineers who have worked on problems somewhat different from mine. Beyond this, I am sure that I can speak intelligibly to scientific and technical men in fields very much further from mine. But can I make myself understood to those whose backgrounds are not scientific, not technical? Can I convey to them also what seems to me to be important about science and technology, and especially about the particular field in which I have worked?

I think that this is possible, but only by being very clear and simple in what one says. I do not think that technical men are bothered by such simplicity, but I have a feeling that others sometimes are. Occasionally, when I have taken great pains to explain an important point to someone unfamiliar with science and have succeeded, I am made to feel that I have failed in some way through my very success. The reaction to understanding finally achieved is sometimes "Oh, that is simple," with an implication that because it can be understood it can't be very important or profound. Such an attitude disregards the fact that brilliant men have failed for centuries to understand just such simple matters, and that only very brilliant men were finally able to make them clear and simple to us, the heirs to their insight.

There is of course another approach to the popularization of science. People sometimes learn from popular books how to string complicated scientific terms together in plausible sequences. None of us is entirely immune to a desire to astound others by a display of this sort. A friend of mine, a very good physicist himself, says that he can talk to "physicists" for as long as half an hour without being found out. By "physicists" he means those who work in newer and more recondite fields than his own. To get away with this sort of thing one must choose his phrases to suit the company. Pat phrases about relativity and the uncertainty principle may impress a lay audience. You had best leave them alone in the presence of physicists. If you are clever with your timing, you can stop a solid-state physicist in his tracks by saying, at the appropriate moment, "It all comes out in the Hamiltonian," or "Of course, it depends on the density of energy levels." For other physicists you must find other pat phrases.

While this approach may make one the life of the party, it is just as likely to mark him as a Mrs. Malaprop or a M. Jourdain. And, indeed, it may lead him to take for a luminary of science someone analogous to the Grand Turk of Molière's comedy.

There is no royal road to science. Those with little or no background can get only a talking knowledge of science by starting first with the most advanced, generalized and difficult aspects of modern physics.

Science has great generalizations. These are highly important and very moving to scientists, for in them the scientist sees summed up many particular phenomena with which he is familiar. Some scientists delight in treating a well-organized subject by presenting it first in its most generalized form and then deducing special instances. This, however, is not the way that things are discovered or the way that things can be learned.

Really to learn anything about science, one must start with simple things which can be easily grasped and understand these thoroughly in the terms of science. In this way the terms acquire precise meaning and become familiar. They come to call up real objects and experiences. For the professional scientist, the experiences may be experiences he has had in the laboratory. For those who have not and will not work in the laboratory, they must be experiences from his life and from his general reading. Once one has mastered some scientific terms and ideas and associated them with the world about him, he can go further afield and study less familiar things and phenomena. As he learns, he will find all about him examples of what he already knows. He will, I think, really come to understand a part of science, though he will not, of course, equip himself to practice it professionally in competition with those who have spent more time in learning.

Many simple phenomena were understood by science centuries ago. Will one not be out of date in starting with this early science? I can reply only that among the scientific tools I use every day in research are Greek mathematics, eighteenth-century mechanics, nineteenth-century electricity and magnetism and twentieth-century relativity. I have even ventured a little into quantum mechanics.

Valid science is never old or out of date. It is only speculation about science, the "application" of science to philosophy, and false analogies between science and other matters that become old almost as soon as they are new. To understand the most recent advances in science without a background of the sound science on which they are built is as ridiculous as it is impossible.

The Scope of This Book

This book is about electronics in a very broad sense of the term. It is not just about electrons in vacuum tubes, although there is a strong emphasis on this narrower aspect of electronics, which once was my field of work. Rather, it is about electronics in the sense of radio, of television, of sending messages across the continent or of locating and guiding planes by radar. The aim of the book is not to present vivid pictures of the size, the cost, the complexity or the wonder of electronic devices or systems, but to give some idea of how they work. To achieve such an understanding, one must understand a variety of things.

Fundamentally, electronics is based upon an understanding of the physical world which gives us some control over it, that is, upon physics. Thus, the reader of this book will find a good deal of physics in it. Much of this will be old, because that is a part of the new. He will find Newton's laws of motion illustrated by the very problems Newton himself solved, but he will also see these laws used in explaining vacuum tubes which are scarcely in commercial use. He will find Faraday's lines of force in the latest electronic devices. Ideas concerning waves which go back to Huygens will be found fundamental to the understanding of microwave antennas, but the propagation of such microwaves will be explained in terms of Maxwell's equations, which belong to the last century.

The operation of some electronic devices, such as transistors, masers and lasers can be explained only by quantum mechanics, and some knowledge of relativity is necessary in order to understand the functioning of a linear accelerator. The old and the new of physics mingle together in electronic devices.

Electronics in a broad sense includes more than devices, and more than physics. It includes putting devices together into systems to accomplish definite purposes. It would be hopeless to try in one book to explain all the things that electronics can do; this includes electronic computing and control devices of enormous variety and complexity as well as communication systems of many sorts. Because it is closest to my background, I have chosen to illustrate electronics at work chiefly in devices which are important in long-distance communication and in radar, though examples such as the electron microscope are given where they fit appropriately.

In our survey of a part of the field of electronics, together with certain side tours, how much can one expect to learn about science and technology in general? Certainly, one will acquire no direct knowledge of biology or chemistry, for instance. One will learn nothing directly about nuclear physics. In the wonderful world of devices one will find no discussions of aerodynamics, of heat engines, of rockets.

Yet, I think that the reader can get more from this book than merely the understanding of something of one part of science and technology. I think he can learn the sorts of problems that science tries to solve, what sort of things science can learn about such problems, and how such knowledge can be organized and applied to solve some of the problems of the world.

The reader can, I hope, learn something of a way of looking at things, something of a frame of mind in which clear understanding even of small and particular problems is valued far above sweeping and appealing statements concerning unclear situations. It is only by approaching the problems of other parts of science and technology with such a background, such a frame of mind, that the reader can make sense of the science and technology of which there is nothing specific in this book.

There remains, then, only to go on to the following chapters. Here, perhaps some specific warnings are necessary. I think an expert in some other field of science or technology will have no trouble with any part of the book. I have tried to make the book intelligible also to the intelligent person whose background in science is almost negligibly small, either because he never learned much mathematics and science or because he didn't like what he learned and has long since forgotten it. Largely for such readers, I have included in the first few chapters material which the expert in another field may well want to skip over.

This material is certain basic, pre-quantum and pre-relativity physics; Newton's laws; electric and magnetic fields; and waves. With the chapter on Maxwell's equations, and perhaps even before, I hope even the expert in another field will find material that is new to him. The expert reader will have to judge for himself what he should read and what he should skip.

The person without scientific background should, however, make every effort to get through the first chapters first. The unpleasant part of swimming is getting into the cold water. The unpleasant part of skiing is the first few awkward tumbles. I am afraid that the chapters immediately following this one may seem to some to be the least interesting ones in this book. It is essential to be familiar with their contents, however. One simply can't talk about electronics without knowing a few words and understanding a few concepts. Getting these may be painful, but it is necessary. I hope that the initial difficulty will not be too great.

There is another hurdle for the non-expert reader. Mathematics is in some degree essential to science. I have tried to explain things largely in words and pictures. However, I have written some things down in the form of equations. In many cases, the equations can be skipped with little loss, although they do enable anyone who might care to, to work out examples for himself. In some cases, as in the case of Maxwell's wonderful equations, the equations are the heart of the matter.

A Review of Algebraic Notation

I have tried, whenever mathematics is necessary, to explain everything in the most elementary terms. Nonetheless, the notation is that of algebra, and this seems an appropriate place to say a few words about it to those who have forgotten some simple matters through years of disuse.

Letters are used to represent various quantities. I will illustrate this by the simple example of the area, A, of a rectangle of height h and width W.

We can say that the area, A, of a rectangle is the product of the height, h, and the width, W. This is the same as saying that A is h times W. Written out as an equation, the statement becomes:

$$A = hW$$

or

$$A = Wh$$

No multiplication sign is used. When one letter follows another, this means to multiply the two quantities.

If the rectangle is 2 feet wide and 4 feet high, we write:

$$A = (2)(4) = 8 \text{ square feet}$$

We use the parentheses as a sort of punctuation; we cannot write 2 times 4 as 24—that means twenty-four.

We sometimes say that a quantity, A, for example, varies *directly* as some other quantity, say, h. This means that the quantity A is something times h. As h grows, or diminishes, W grows or diminishes in proportion, so that if h is doubled, W will double. In the case we have been considering, A is W times h, so that A varies directly as h. It also varies directly as W.

Division is always written as a fraction. Thus, the statement that h is A divided by W is written:

$$h = \frac{A}{W}$$

We would read this, "h equals A over W." In a relation like this, we say that h varies *inversely* as W. This merely means h is equal to something divided by W. As W grows, h diminishes, and vice versa, and if W is doubled, h is halved.

If the rectangle is a square, and the length of each side is l, then

$$A = (l)(l) = l^2$$

The symbol l^2 (*l* squared) is simply the product, *l* and *l*.

Sometimes we say that a quantity varies *inversely as the square* of another quantity. In the equation

$$F = \frac{g}{r^2}$$

the quantity *F* varies inversely as the square of *r*. In this case, if we double *r*, *F* is one fourth as great.

In the case of a square whose sides have a length *l* and whose area is *A*, we can write:

$$l = \sqrt{A}$$

This says that *l* is the square root of *A*. $\sqrt{A}$ multiplied by $\sqrt{A}$, that is, the square of the square root of *A*, is equal to *A*.

$$(\sqrt{A})\,(\sqrt{A}) = (\sqrt{A})^2 = A$$

in a numerical example,

$$(\sqrt{2})(\sqrt{2}) = (\sqrt{2})^2 = 2$$

The square root of 2 is approximately 1.414.

In using letters to represent quantities we sometimes use the same letter with subscripts to denote different quantities of the same sort. Thus, if we had three circles of different radii, we might use

$$r_1,\ r_2,\ r_3$$

to denote the different radii. r_1 might be the radius of the first of the three circles, r_2 of the second, and r_3 of the third. Sometimes the subscripts are letters, as:

$$f_n,\ f_p$$

Here n in connection with f_n may mean the component of the force f *normal* (perpendicular) to some direction, and f_p may be the component of force *parallel* to that direction. The meaning of these particular terms will be made clearer in Chapter Two.

Relations between Numbers

In the equations of mathematics and physics, certain numbers recur over and over again. The most common and the most venerable of these is represented by the Greek letter π (pi). It is the ratio of the circumference of a circle to the diameter of the circle. More often, we shall talk about the radius of a circle, or a sphere, which we may call r.

If r is the radius of a circle, the circumference, S, of the circle is

$$S = 2\pi r$$

If r is the radius of a circle, the area, A, of the circle is given by

$$A = \pi r^2$$

If r is the radius of a sphere, the area, A, of the surface of the sphere is given by

$$A = 4\pi r^2$$

The number π is represented symbolically by a letter because it cannot be expressed in numbers with perfect accuracy, no matter how many digits we use. When we come to make calculations we use an approximate value which is accurate enough. To three significant figures we can use for π either 3.14, or the old schoolboy approximation, 22/7.

Engineers and physicists, as well as mathematicians, make use of negative numbers such as -2 (minus 2) as well as positive numbers such as $+2$ (plus 2); $+2$ is also written simply 2. Negative numbers are used because negative numbers make it more convenient to describe physical quantities; height, for example. Instead of having to say 2 feet *above* or 2 feet *below*, we need use only one word, height. We can let a height of $+2$ feet mean 2 feet above and a height of -2 feet mean 2 feet below.

Suppose, for instance, we reckon height above the surface of the ocean. Suppose that we raise an object a feet and then b feet more; we increase its height, h, by $a + b$ feet, so we write:

$$h = a + b$$

Suppose as an example that we raise the object 10 feet and lower it 5 feet. We can use the same formula for its final height if we represent the raising and lowering by:

$$a = 10,$$
$$b = -5,$$
$$h = 10 + (-5) = 5$$

When we add a negative number to a positive number we take the difference and use the sign of the larger number.

What if we raise the object 5 feet and lower it 10 feet? We then say:

$$a = 5,$$
$$b = -10,$$
$$h = 5 - 10 = -5$$

This indicates that the object ends up 5 feet below the surface, which is just right.

The reader will have to take my word for the fact that, in order to get consistent results using negative numbers, we must say that the product of two negative numbers is a positive number, while multiplying a negative number and a positive number gives a negative number.

The use of negative numbers is a convenience. When we use them we don't have to use several terms, as, both *height* and *depth*, nor write the equations several ways for several cases.

We have seen how relations between numbers can be represented by equations such as

$$A = hW$$

Relations between numbers can also be represented by graphs, and a particular curve will correspond to a particular equation.

For example, suppose, as shown in Fig. 1, that distance up or down from the horizontal line or *axis* is y, and distance to the right or left of the vertical axis is x. When this is so, the horizontal line is called the x axis and the vertical line is called the y axis. A positive value of x means some distance to the right of the y axis; a negative value of x means some distance to the left of the y axis. Similarly, a positive value of y means some distance above the x axis, while a negative value of y means some distance below the x axis.

Let us see how this works out in the case of the equation

$$y = 1.5x$$

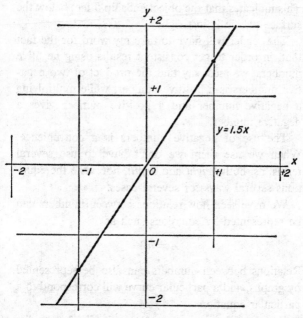

Figure 1

The table below shows some pairs of values of x and y that, as the reader can verify, satisfy this equation:

y	x
−1.5	−1.0
−1.2	−.8
−.75	−.5
0	0
.75	.5
1.2	.8
1.5	1.0

The first pair of values, $y = -1.5$, $x = -1.0$, is represented by a point 1.5 units below the x axis and 1 unit to the left of the y axis. The reader can easily see that all the points given in the table lie on the slanting straight line of Fig. 1. The line corresponds to or represents the equation $y = 1.5x$: the equation corresponds to or represents the line. An equation such as this one, in which one *variable* (y in this case) is a constant (1.5 in this case) times another variable (x in this case), is called a *linear* equation because it is represented by a straight line.

Not all equations are linear. Consider the equation

$$y = .5x^2$$

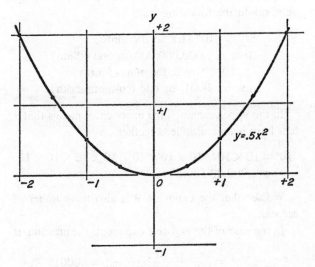

Figure 2

The values of x and y in the table below satisfy this equation:

y	x
2	-2
.5	-1
0	0
.5	1
2	2

The curve corresponding to this equation (the values of y and x in the table of course lie on the curve) is shown in Fig. 2. This curve is called a *parabola*.

Sometimes mathematicians, scientists and engineers have to deal with very large or very small numbers. In expressing large numbers, I have often said "a billion billion" or some such thing. Physicists write large numbers in the following way:

$$10^9 \text{ (ten to the ninth)}$$
(that is, 1,000,000,000, or one billion)
$$10^{-4} \text{ (ten to the minus fourth)}$$
(that is, .0001, or one ten-thousandth)

In the upper example, the exponent 9 means that 9 tens have been multiplied together.

$$10^9 = 10 \times 10 \times 10 \times 10 \times 10 \times 10 \times 10 \times 10 \times 10$$
$$= 1,000,000,000$$

We see that the exponent 9 is also the number of zeroes.

In the case of the negative exponent, the meaning is

$$10^{-4} = \frac{1}{10 \times 10 \times 10 \times 10} = .0001$$

The negative exponent tells how many times we divide by 10.

A particular number will be written as follows, using the × sign for multiplication:

$$2.38 \times 10^5 \quad \text{(meaning 238,000)}$$
$$9.0 \times 10^{-2} \quad \text{(meaning .090)}$$

We write 9.0 to show that the quantity is accurate to two significant figures. That is, we guarantee only that the value is nearer to 9.0 than it is to 8.9 or to 9.1; it might be 8.98 or 9.04, for instance.

There is one more matter connected with the equations in the text. Some rare reader may wish to use the equations to make calculations. While I mention a variety of units, such as feet, pounds, and centimeters, the equations are all valid in the M.K.S. (meter-kilogram-second) system of units. In an appendix at the end of the book these are related to feet, pounds, and other familiar units, and numerical values are given for various constants which are represented by letters in the equations quoted in the text.

Chapter Two

THE LAWS OF MOTION

Two great universal phenomena which must be understood in order to understand electronics are the motions of particles—that is, very small bodies—and the motion of waves. Waves we shall consider in Chapter Five. The particles with which electronics deals are chiefly electrons. These are tiny particles with a negative charge. Sometimes in electronics we deal with positive or negative ions. These are atoms or molecules which have lost an electron from their makeup, leaving a net positive charge (positive ions), or to which an extra electron has become attached (negative ions). In electronics ions may be produced when electrons strike atoms or molecules. They may also be produced when short electromagnetic waves, such as ultraviolet light or X rays, strike the molecules of a gas.

In order to understand the motion of electrons or ions through the emptiness of a vacuum tube, we must have some understanding of the laws of motion, laws which govern not only the motion of electrons and of ions in vacuum tubes but all motions in the world about us and the motions of heavenly bodies as well: the motions of baseballs and automobiles, the motions of satellites and planets in their orbits, and the motions of the stars in their courses.

To one familiar with the laws of motion, they come to seem simple and obvious. Certainly they are not obvious, for they eluded thoughtful and intelligent men for many centuries. Indeed, recently, during a trip by air, the man in the seat next to mine marveled that when he dropped a pencil in the plane it did not fall behind on its way to the floor. I explained to him that in the seventeenth century Newton stated that a body continues at rest or in uniform motion in a straight line unless it is acted on by a force, and that this law explained the behavior of the dropped pencil.

The laws of motion do not seem obvious except to those who are familiar with them, and, while they are simple, motion as we see it in the world about us certainly is not. The objects we see about us are complicated and the forces acting on them are many and varied. The objects themselves are complicated in shape and structure, and they exhibit rotations and distortions in form as well as motion as a whole from place to place. Of the forces acting on them, some, like the gusty wind, vary with time; some, like the drag of water on a boat, vary in a complicated way with velocity; some, like the friction on a box dragged along the ground, vary from place to place. Thus, the most competent mathematician or physicist would be sorely puzzled to analyze in detail almost any everyday example of motion. It is for this reason that the laws of motion eluded natural philosophers for so long.

Even in relatively simple cases, motion proved difficult to understand. Our common experience is that all motion naturally tends to cease unless some mover maintains it. The motions of the heavens seem eternal. This led early philosophers to look for a prime mover as the cause of this motion of heavenly bodies instead of regarding the unceasing motion of the heavens as a clue to the understanding of sublunar phenomena.

There are, however, a few common examples of motion which can be understood in detail as well as in principle. Most of these examples are to be found in man-made machines—in automobiles, in airplanes, or in vacuum tubes. Perhaps the simplest and most beautiful motions are those of planets and stars, which wheel through the vacuum of space free of friction that would slow their progress and are acted on only by their mutual gravitational attractions. Among the most fruitful examples of motion we can analyze are the motions of electrons in vacuum tubes, and we will talk about these in due time.

It is best, however, to proceed from the familiar to the unfamiliar. Henri Poincaré, who was perhaps the greatest mathematician of the latter part of the nineteenth century and the early part of the twentieth, pointed out that even in as abstract a science as mathematics one should cultivate an intuitive appreciation of concepts such as straightness, although one must check and guide intuition by formal proofs. It is even more important to have an intuitive feel for the laws of physics, so that they do not remain abstract patterns of words but rather call up a host of familiar instances of the actual observable behavior of physical systems.

Skating: An Example of the Laws of Motion

To the professional scientist, many of these instances that make the laws of physics real are things with which he is familiar in the laboratory. To one who does not have a background of laboratory work they must come from the observable world about us. Hence, in introducing the laws of motion it is much better at first to consider familiar objects rather than such a tiny, unfamiliar, unseeable, and almost unbelievable particle as the electron.

Among the rare examples of simple and easily understood motions which we encounter in everyday life is skating. Skating offers a fine example of the laws of motion, for the friction which slows our progress is small, and we are willing to accept the pressure of the wind as a force to be accounted for separately. Too, the ice is level, so that the force of gravity does not enter into consideration. In fact, you slide on straight ahead, just as Newton asserted two centuries ago, unless some easily identified force changes your speed or the direction of your motion. When this happens you can feel the force very clearly. Someone may push you from behind: you can feel him pushing; you observe that you go faster. You may run into someone. You feel the pressure that slows you down as you come to an abrupt stop.

If you are a little more skillful, you may suddenly turn your skates sideways, edge on. As you lean against the force of the ice on the skates, they shave the surface, and the sideways force of the surface against them brings you to a stop. If, however, the skates are turned less abruptly, you go around a smooth curve with undiminished speed; the force which you feel, and which causes you to lean lest it topple you over, changes the direction rather than the speed of your motion. If, while skating along past a smooth upright pole, you grab it and swing around it so as to reverse your direction, you feel even more strongly the force that changes your motion from that motion of constant speed in a straight line which, as Newton assured us, will persist unless a force acts.

At any instant a moving body has a particular direction of motion even if the body is traveling along a curved path. Fig. 3 shows the path of a body moving from A to D. The arrowheads indicate which way the body is moving along the curve. Just as the body is passing some intermediate point, B, its direction of motion is the direction of b–b', the tangent to the path at the point B. The tangent is a line which just touches the curved path at one point, point B in this case. As the body passes some other point, C, the velocity will be in the direction of the tangent to the path at that point, c–c'.

At every point such as B or C the body has a speed of motion as well as a direction of motion. The speed of motion may be measured in feet per second, miles per hour, or some other units. We get this speed by dividing a small distance that the body moves by the time it takes to traverse that small distance.

Vectors

When physicists speak of the velocity of a body, they refer not only to its speed at a point in its path but to its direction of motion as well. Physicists represent the velocity of a body, whether it be a human body, a planet or an electron, by an arrow. Two such arrows, v_B and v_C, corresponding to the velocities at points B and C, are shown in Fig. 3. The length of such an arrow is proportional to the speed, in feet per

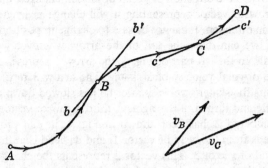

Figure 3

second, miles per hour, meters per second, or other units. The arrow points in the direction of motion. If the speed is doubled, the arrow is made twice as long. If the direction of motion changes, the direction of the arrow is changed. The motion represented by the arrow, and the arrow itself representing the motion, are called *vectors*. Because the arrow represents the velocity of, say, a man or an electron, we are tempted to draw it with its head or its tail at the position of the man or of the electron. We can do so if we like, but usually, as in Fig. 3, we do not. The arrow represents the *speed* and *direction* of motion, but *not* the *position* of the moving body. We can if we wish draw the arrow representing the velocity in a fixed place as the body moves about. In Fig. 3 the arrows or vectors v_B and v_C, representing the velocities at points B and C, have been drawn from a single point. This is just as reasonable as it would be to have (by remote radio control) a speedometer always in one place which would indicate the speed of a car as it traveled away across the country.

When the direction or speed of motion changes, the arrow or vector representing it will change in length or in direction. It cannot be said to change in position, for we can draw the tail of the arrow wherever we wish. In the left part of Fig. 4, the arrow 1 represents the original velocity of a skater. The arrow 3 represents the skater's velocity after he has slowed down a little and turned to the right. A third arrow or vector, numbered 2, has been drawn in Fig. 4; its tail proceeds from the head of vector 1, and its head is at the head of vector 3. This vector 2 represents the change in velocity, both in speed and in direction, as the skater turns and slows down. The final velocity, 3, is called the *vector sum* of the original velocity, 1, and the change in velocity, 2. The vector sum of two vectors is always obtained by connecting the vectors, tail to head. The vector sum is then a vector with its tail at the free tail and its head at the free head, just as in the left part of Fig. 4.

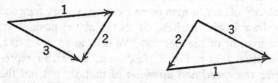

Figure 4

Suppose we added vectors 1 and 2 in the other order, placing the head of 2 to the tail of 1, as in the right of Fig. 4. Remembering that it is only the magnitude and direction of a vector and not its position that is important, we see that we get the same vector sum, 3, as in the left of Fig. 4. The vector sum does not depend on the order in which vectors are added.

Sometimes, one adds many vectors together to obtain a vector sum, as shown in Fig. 5. Here the vectors 1, 2, 3, 4 are shown added together in two different orders to obtain the same vector sum, vector 5. By one of the most elementary rules of geometry, two joined vectors always lie in a plane, or flat surface. When we have three or more vectors to add, they will not in general lie in the same plane, as they have been drawn in the simple sketch of Fig. 5.

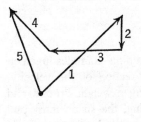
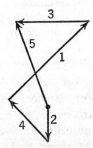

Figure 5

The first of Newton's laws says that motion proceeds at a constant speed in a straight line unless a force acts. His second law says that when the velocity does change, the force that changes it acts in the direction of the change in velocity (in the direction of vector 2 in Figs. 4 and 5) and that the force times the interval of time during which it acts is proportional to the magnitude of the change in velocity, that is, to the length of the vector 2. Thus, a given force acting for a given time might cause the skater to turn without speeding up. In this case, the vectors representing the initial and final velocities and the change in velocity would look as shown to the left in Fig. 6. Or, the same force acting for the same time might cause the skater to speed up without turning, as shown in the right of Fig. 6. In each case, the change in velocity—that is, the arrow or vector 2—has the same length, which is proportional to the strength or magnitude of the force multiplied by the time during which it acts.

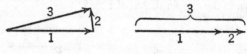

Figure 6

We can easily think of common examples in which a force changes only the direction of the velocity. For instance, when we swing a weight around and around at the end of a string, the string must pull inward on the weight to keep it going in a circle. If the string broke, the weight would continue in a straight line (except that gravity would cause it to fall). If we want the weight to turn continually, and so to change direction continually, as it must in going around a circle, we must apply a force normal (at right angles) to its direction of motion, and that is just what the string does. We could, if we wished, fasten the string to a spring scale and measure the force needed to keep the weight circling.

The effect we see in whirling a weight about on a string is the same effect we experience in a car going around a corner. Our body tends to continue on in a straight line, and it is only because the seat or door presses sidewise against us that we are able to turn with the car. The bicycle rider, the runner, the skater, lean when they turn so that the ground may not only support them but push them toward the center of the circle in which they turn. In the huge spinning bowl used as an amusement device the walls push in against the people so that their velocities may be changed continually as they travel in a circular path.

We can also think of common examples in which a force acts to change the magnitude of the velocity without changing its direction. When a car accelerates on a straightaway, the wheels push against the road. In turn, the back of the seat presses against the driver's back and causes him to gain speed as rapidly as the car. In diving from the edge of a pool a swimmer gains speed by pushing back with his legs.

In all of these examples the change of velocity is in the direction of the applied force and the magnitude of the change in velocity is proportional to the force times the time during which it acts. The change in velocity per second is called the *acceleration*, and Newton's second law states that the force required to produce a given acceleration of a body is the *mass* times the acceleration. This may be written as an equation:

$$f = ma$$

Here f is force, m is mass, and a is acceleration. If velocity is measured in feet per second, acceleration will be measured in feet per second per second.

The force of gravity, which causes a falling body to gain speed, offers another example of a force that can act in the direction of motion to increase the speed of a body. If we hang a body on a scale, we can measure the force of gravity; this force is called the weight of the body, and it is proportional to the body's mass.

If we release the body, this force of weight causes the body to fall downward. As both the weight (which is the force accelerating the body) and the force required to give a body a given acceleration are proportional to the mass of the body, the acceleration of a freely falling body is independent of its mass. This is what Galileo may or may not have demonstrated at the Leaning Tower of Pisa. Disregarding air resistance, any falling body gains velocity at a rate of 32.2 feet per second for each second of fall. This acceleration of 32.2 feet per second per second is called the acceleration of gravity at the earth's surface.

The force of gravity, which causes a dropped body to fall, can also cause a body to curve in its path. When we throw a ball, it rises for a while and then begins to fall downward; the curve it follows is called a *parabola*. If an object is thrown upward fast enough it will rise forever and escape from the gravitational attraction of the earth, as several space shots, including the voyage of Mariner to the vicinity of Venus, have demonstrated. The velocity required is about 7 miles a second. And the moon circles the earth, perpetually drawn from the straight path it would otherwise follow if there were no gravitational attraction of the earth.

Newton's Law of Gravitation

It was, in fact, by means of the motion of the moon around the earth that Newton checked his idea of a universal law of gravitation. At first he was doubtful about his proposed law because the moon's distance was not known correctly, and the proposed law appeared to be wrong. Some twenty years later, the moon's distance was measured more accurately, and calculations based on these new data fitted Newton's laws.

Because this example illustrates so beautifully both the laws of motion and the law of gravitation, it seems worthwhile to go through it in detail.

In order to understand the motion of the moon, we must state Newton's law of gravitation. Newton's way of stating this was to say that two particles of matter attract one another with a force which lies in the direction of the line connecting the particles and whose magnitude is proportional to the product of the masses of the particles and inversely proportional to the square of the distance between them.

A particle is a body so tiny that we can disregard its size and shape. The earth and moon are not particles, but Newton was able to show that a spherical body attracts another spherical body as if the mass of each sphere were located at its center. Thus, Newton's law applies to the earth and the moon, which are nearly spherical, if we measure distance center to center. We can state Newton's law of gravitation as an equation if we wish:

$$f = g \frac{m_a m_b}{r^2}$$

Here f is force, g is a *constant*, m_a and m_b are the two masses, and r is the distance between them. When we apply this law to different cases the masses m_a and m_b will be different, and we might designate the masses by different subscripts. The distance between the masses, r, and the force f may vary with time. But g is always the same, at any time, at any place in the universe (so far as we know). That is why g is called a constant, and its value will be found in tables of physical constants.

For our purposes it will be a little more convenient merely to examine the form of this law in order to see how great the acceleration of gravity will be at various distances from the center of the earth. The mass m_e of the earth would produce a force f_1 on some object of mass m_0 at a distance r_1 from the center of the earth, and would produce a force f_2 on the same object of mass m_0 at a distance r_2 from the center of the earth. From the law of gravitation, we see that the ratio of these two forces will be

$$\frac{f_2}{f_1} = \frac{(gm_em_0/r_2{}^2)}{(gm_em_0/r_1{}^2)} = \frac{r_1{}^2}{r_2{}^2} = \left(\frac{r_1}{r_2}\right)^2$$

Now, the force f_2 is a_2, the acceleration of gravity at the radius r_2 times the mass m_0, and the force f_1 is a_1, the acceleration of gravity at the radius r_1, times the mass m_0. Hence

$$\frac{f_2}{f_1} = \frac{m_0a_2}{m_0a_1} = \left(\frac{r_1}{r_2}\right)^2$$

From this we easily see that

$$a_2 = a_1\left(\frac{r_1}{r_2}\right)^2$$

Now we can let a_1 be 32.2 feet per second per second, the acceleration of gravity at the earth's surface, whose radius r_1 is the 3960 miles from the surface to the center of the earth. The radius r_2 of the moon's orbit is 238,000 miles. Thus, the acceleration a_2 of the earth's gravity at the moon's orbit must be

$$32.2 \left(\frac{3,960}{238,000} \right)^2 = .00892 \text{ feet per second per second}$$

Newton asked, does this actually correspond to the observed acceleration of the moon in its orbit?

The actual path of the moon is slightly elliptical, but we will consider it to be a circle with the mean radius of the ellipse, that is, 238 thousand miles or 1257 million feet. The circumference of the orbit is 2π times this, that is, 7900 million feet. The moon travels around this orbit in a period of 27.2 days or 2.35 million seconds. Thus, its orbital velocity is 3360 feet per second.

As the moon moves around the earth, its velocity continually changes in direction. At full moon the moon is outside the earth's orbit and is moving parallel to the earth in its orbit, and in the same direction. Seven days later, at waning half-moon, the moon is moving toward the sun. Seven days later still, at the dark of the moon, the moon is between the earth and the sun and it is moving contrary to the direction of the earth in its orbit. Seven days later still, at waxing half-moon, the moon is moving away from the sun. These successive positions of the moon with respect to the earth and the sun are shown at the left in Fig. 7. The diagram is drawn looking down on the plane of the moon's orbit from above the earth's north pole, that is, looking south. Arrowheads show the direction of motion of the moon in its orbit, and a circular segment with an arrowhead shows the direction of rotation of the earth.

I also have shown, in the left-hand part of Fig. 7, vectors representing the velocity of the moon at each of four phases. These vectors have their tails at the position of the moon at each phase. This placement is allowable because the position of a vector may be chosen as one wishes. Vector v_1 represents the velocity of the moon in its orbit at full moon. Vector v_2 represents the velocity of the moon at the waning half. Vector v_3 represents the velocity of the moon at the dark of the moon. Vector v_4 represents the velocity of the moon at the waxing half.

As the position of these vectors is purely arbitrary, in the right of Fig. 7 I have redrawn the vectors v_1 through v_4 as radiating from a common center. The diagram in the right of Fig. 7 is a vector diagram representing *velocities*. The arrows do not show the positions of the moon; these are shown in the corresponding diagram of *positions*, in the left of Fig. 7. For each position of the moon in the left of Fig. 7 the moon will have some particular velocity, represented by an arrow radiating from the center of the velocity diagram at the right of Fig. 7.

I have shown in the right of Fig. 7 vectors representing the velocities of the moon at a number of intermediate phases as well as at full, waning half, dark, and waxing half. Thus, as the moon moves in the position diagram successively from the position at full moon through two successive intermediate positions to waning half, the corresponding velocities at successive positions are v_1 (at full), v_a, v_b, and v_2 (at waning half), as shown to the right in Fig. 7. The velocity v_a is the vector sum of the velocity v_1 at full and a *change in velocity* shown as v_I in the right of Fig. 7.

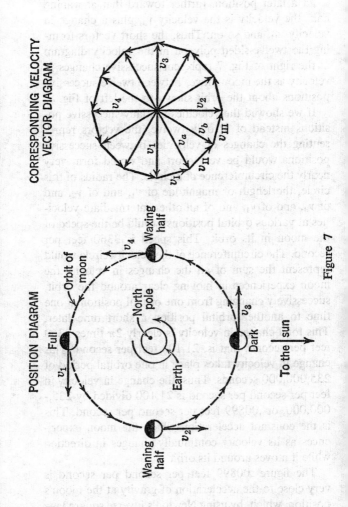

CORRESPONDING VELOCITY VECTOR DIAGRAM

v_3
v_4
v_2
v_a
v_b
v_{III}
v_1
v_{II}
v_I

POSITION DIAGRAM

Full
v_1
Orbit of moon
Waxing half
v_4
North pole
Earth
To the sun
v_3
Dark
v_2
Waning half

Figure 7

At a later position, further toward that at waning half, the velocity is the velocity v_a, plus a change in velocity v_{II}, and so on. Thus, the short vectors forming the twelve-sided polygon in the velocity diagram at the right of Fig. 7 represent successive changes in velocity as the moon moves between twelve successive positions about the orbit shown to the left of Fig. 7.

If we showed the velocities at many successive positions instead of at only twelve, the vectors representing the changes of velocities between successive positions would be very short and would form very nearly the circumference of a circle. The radius of this circle, the length or magnitude of v_1, and of v_2, and of v_3, and of v_4, and of all other intermediate velocities at various orbital positions, would be the speed of the moon in its orbit. This speed is 3360 feet per second. The circumference of the velocity circle would represent the sum of all the changes in velocity the moon experiences in moving clear around the orbit, successively changing from one orbital position at one time to another orbital position a short time later. This total change in velocity is clearly 2π times 3360 feet per second, that is, 21,100 feet per second. This change in velocity takes place in one orbital period of 235,000,000 seconds. Thus, the change in velocity in feet per second per second is 21,100 divided by 235,-000,000, or .00899 feet per second per second. This is the constant acceleration which the moon experiences as its velocity continually changes in direction while it moves around its orbit.

The figure .00899 feet per second per second is very close to the acceleration of gravity at the moon's position, which, by using Newton's inverse square law, we earlier computed to be .00892 feet per second per second. According to Newton's second law, the acceleration of the moon in its orbit should be equal to the acceleration of gravity at the moon's position. Inaccuracies in our assumptions account for the small discrepancy. The moon does not actually revolve about the earth's center, but about the mutual center of mass of the moon and the earth, which lies within the earth but a little toward the moon. Further, the moon's orbit is not exactly circular.

When we look back to see what we have done, we see that the acceleration of a body in a circular orbit can be written in several forms; for instance:

$$a = \frac{2\pi v}{T} = \frac{v^2}{r} = \frac{(2\pi)^2 r}{T^2}$$

These various forms, which involve the orbital velocity v, the orbital period T, and the orbital radius r, are related by the fact that the velocity is the circumference of the orbit divided by the orbital period; that is,

$$v = \frac{2\pi r}{T}$$

Through astronomical observations and by the application of Newton's laws we can measure the masses of the planets which have satellites. To see how this may be done, let us consider a particular case. Astronomical observations tell us that Jupiter's satellite Io is 262,000 miles, or 1380 million feet, from the center of Jupiter and has an orbital period of 1.77 days, or 153 thousand seconds. The acceleration, $(2\pi)^2 r/T^2$, is thus 2.34 feet per second per second. This must be the acceleration of Jupiter's gravity at Io's orbit.

At the surface of the earth, 3960 miles from the

center, the acceleration of the earth's gravity is 32.2 feet per second per second. At the same distance from earth as Io is from Jupiter, by Newton's inverse square law of gravitation the acceleration of the earth's gravity would be .00736 feet per second per second. Our observations have enabled us to calculate that the acceleration of Jupiter's gravity at this same distance from Jupiter is 2.34 feet per second per second, or 318 times as great. Newton's law of gravitation tells us that the acceleration of gravity at a given distance from an object is proportional to the mass of the object, so we conclude that Jupiter's mass must be 318 times as great as that of the earth.

Newton's laws of motion and of gravitation changed astronomy from an empirical to a theoretical science. Newton showed that Kepler's laws governing the motions of the planets in their elliptical orbits are consequences of the laws of motion. The open parabolic orbits and hyperbolic orbits in which some comets approach the sun and leave it again, never to return, were deduced from Newton's laws. By the beginning of the nineteenth century, Laplace* had shown that the planets are stable in their orbits about the sun despite the perturbing forces they exert on one another, and the solar system seemed to be reduced to an eternal, frictionless machine.

Using Newton's Laws of Motion

Today, save in exceptional cases involving relativity, astronomers no longer test Newton's laws; they

---

* Pierre Simon, Marquis de Laplace (1749–1827) was a great French mathematician whose classic works included a detailed study of the Newtonian mechanics of the solar system.

use them. They use them to calculate the motions of stars, satellites and comets, and to explain such phenomena as tides. Engineers use them to calculate the orbits of missiles, communication satellites and space vehicles.

I think that a few examples are in order. Echo I is, at this writing, in a nearly circular orbit at an altitude of about 1000 miles, or a radius of 4960 miles or 2.62×10^7 feet where, according to our equations, the acceleration of the earth's gravity is 20.5 feet per second per second. Syncom II is in a circular orbit at an altitude of 22,300 miles, or a radius of 26,260 miles or 1.387×10^8 feet, where the acceleration of the earth's gravity is .734 feet per second per second. We can see from the equation in this chapter relating orbital radius, acceleration and orbital period that the orbital period of Echo I is 7090 seconds or 118 minutes, while the orbital period of Syncom II is 8.62×10^4 seconds or 24.0 hours. It is because Syncom II revolves around the earth in one day (or, correctly, in one sidereal day) that it does not change progressively in longitude with time. Rather, it just keeps up with the rotation of the earth.

We have come a great way in understanding the laws of motion; in fact, we have covered most of what we need to know in order to understand how electrons travel through vacuum tubes. There are, however, vital things which we have not discussed, and which it would be a shame to miss.

Newton's first law of motion states that a body remains at rest or in motion in a straight line with constant velocity unless it is acted on by a force. Newton's second law states that when a body is acted on by a force, the change in velocity lies in the direction of the force, and the magnitude of the change in velocity is proportional to the period of time during which the force acts times the force (the change will be twice as great for the same mass if we double the force) and is inversely proportional to the mass (the change will be half as great for a given force and time if we double the mass).

Newton had something else to say about motion. He said in his third law that every action has an equal and opposite reaction. By this he meant that if a body *A* exerts a force on a body *B*, then body *B* exerts an equal and opposite force on body *A*. If I push a skater, who feels a force pushing him ahead, I feel the skater's back pushing back against my hands. The same principle is illustrated by the kick of a gun when it shoots out a bullet. If I am gliding on skates and bump into the back of another skater who is going in the same direction, a force acts which speeds him up, and an equal and opposite force acts which slows me down.

Momentum and Angular Momentum

The product of the mass of a body times its velocity is called the *momentum* of the body. The momentum is a vector, just like the velocity, and it has the same direction as the velocity. From Newton's laws of motion, including the equality of action and reaction, a *theorem* called the *conservation of momentum* can be proved by mathematical manipulation. This theorem states that if we consider together all of a set of bodies which exert forces on one another, and if we add the *momenta* (plural of *momentum*) of all these bodies, the vector sum of these momenta, which is the momentum of the system as a whole, is a constant, and does not change during all the complicated motions which the mutually interacting bodies undergo. Should we momentarily intervene from outside and push any one of the interacting bodies so as to change its momentum, the momentum of the system is changed by the same amount, and the new momentum is henceforward conserved.

The conservation of momentum is a fundamental and vital part of physics. With the years, it has been generalized to include the non-mechanical momentum of electromagnetic waves. The conservation of momentum will not concern us much in connection with simple motions of electrons, because we are usually interested only in the tiny forces necessary to change the motions of electrons themselves in the manner we desire. We are little interested in the forces which the electrons exert in return. The case is a good deal like that of jumping straight up from the surface of the earth. The conservation of momentum tells us that when we attain a certain upward velocity and upward momentum, the earth must move downward with such a velocity as to give it an equal and opposite momentum. The earth is very massive compared with you or me, and as momentum is mass times velocity, the velocity with which the earth moves down when you or I jump up is very small; ordinarily, we simply disregard it. In the same way, a vacuum tube is much heavier than billions of electrons, and we don't worry about the forces that the electrons exert on the structure of the tube.

The case is different in astronautics. In that field engineers are working actively on ion propulsion devices, intended to push space vehicles forward by means of a beam of heavy ions rather than by means of the hot gases of a rocket motor. The thrusts which have been attained have been very small, but in principle such electrically powered devices can operate for very long periods of time with the expenditure of little material compared with rockets, and they may be useful in long space flights outside the earth's atmosphere.

Equally important with the conservation of momentum is the *conservation of angular momentum*. When the moon moves around the earth, the magnitude of its angular momentum is its distance from the earth times its mass times its velocity in its orbit (assuming the orbit to be circular). More generally, for noncircular motion, to obtain the angular momentum of a particle about a given point we first connect the point and the particle with a straight line. We then find the component of the particle's momentum normal to this line, and we multiply this component of momentum by the length of the line; this operation gives the magnitude of the angular momentum. The meaning of *component* will be made clear shortly. Angular momentum is a vector, and its direction lies normal to both the line connecting the point and the particle and to the component of momentum normal to the line. Thus, the vector representing the moon's angular momentum about the earth lies normal to the moon's orbit.

Like linear momentum, the angular momentum of a system of bodies acting on one another is conserved. If we broadjump west to east, we gain a certain angular momentum, and the earth slows in its rotation from west to east just enough to lose an equal amount of angular momentum.

When a skater whirls about, arms outstretched, and then draws his arms in, he spins faster—angular momentum is conserved. Since the angular momentum of his arms is proportional to their velocity times their distance from the center of rotation, when the skater draws his arms closer to his center of rotation they must move faster in order for the product of velocity and radius to remain constant. Acrobats hanging by their teeth also speed up their whirling by drawing in their arms.

It is perhaps more striking to note that the angular momentum of the moon revolving about the earth plus the angular momentum of the earth turning on its axis is conserved. The friction of the tides, which are caused in the earth's seas by the pull of the moon, continually slows down the rotation of the earth. This slowing down continually speeds up the revolution of the moon in its orbit. The speeding up causes the moon to recede from the earth at a rate of 5 feet per century. Eventually, the rotation of the earth and the revolution of the moon will have the same period. Thereafter, the smaller solar tidal effect, which we have hitherto disregarded, will slow the common speed of revolution and rotation, and the moon will slowly fall toward the earth. This event lies so far in the future that it need not seriously concern us.

Angular momentum is also extremely important in connection with nuclear physics. Each elementary particle of physics, such as the proton and the neutron, has an angular momentum called *spin*. Total angular momentum, that is, the total spin, plus the angular momenta of particles with respect to one another, as well as the total linear momentum of the particles in their motions, must be conserved in nuclear reactions in which particles and photons change bewilderingly into other particles and photons.

We have dealt with the dynamics only of particles, that is, of tiny bodies of negligible dimensions. When many particles are held rigidly together, the motion of the whole consists of *rotation* as well as of *translation*. The astonishing behavior of the gyroscope is an example of a rigid body following Newton's laws of motion. The reader will have to look elsewhere and to think very hard in order to understand this and many other fascinating aspects of the motion of rigid bodies.

The Law of Conservation of Energy

While we will be little concerned with the conservation of momentum and the conservation of angular momentum in connection with electronic devices, there is another law that can be deduced from Newton's laws of motion which we cannot disregard. This is the law of conservation of energy.

In order to understand the law of conservation of energy we must know what a *component of velocity* is. Suppose that vector v in Fig. 8 is the velocity of a body at some instant. Suppose that vector f of Fig. 8 is the force acting on the body. We can represent f as the sum of two vectors f_p and f_n which, added vectorially, equal f. These two vectors f_p and f_n together *are* the force—for, added, they are equal to the force f; this is as true as that 2 plus 3 is 5; $2 + 3$ is just another way of writing 5, and f_p plus f_n is just another way of writing f.

In Fig. 8, f_p and f_n have been chosen so that the component of force f_p is parallel to the velocity v, and

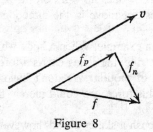

Figure 8

the component of force f_n is normal to the velocity v. f_p is the component of the force f which acts in the direction of motion of the body, and f_n is the component of the force f which acts normal to the motion of the body. f_p acts to speed the body up; f_n acts to turn the body in its path without changing its speed. The force may be so directed that the component parallel to the velocity points in the opposite direction from the velocity, as shown in Fig. 9. The component f_p may then be said to be negative, and it acts to slow the body down.

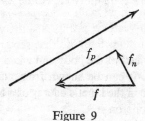

Figure 9

In mechanics, *work* is defined as force exerted in direction of motion times distance of motion. Work is the component of force in the direction of motion, f_p, times the distance the body moves while the force acts. The force f_n does no work on the body, because the body does not move in the direction in which f_n acts.

Think of an example. When a body whirls about at the end of a string, the string exerts a force normal to the direction of motion. We don't have to do work in applying this force; we could merely tie the string to a fixed pivot.

When we push a skater ahead, however, we exert a force in the direction of motion. We speed the skater up, and we do work (and get tired) in so doing.

The earth does no work on the moon in holding it in its orbit, but it does do work on a falling apple as the apple falls.

Work is force in the direction of motion times distance moved. We can write it:

$$W = f_p l$$

Here W stands for work, f_p for force in the direction of motion, and l for distance moved. Work done on a freely moving body changes its speed.

We can define a quantity called the *kinetic energy*, E_k, of a body:

$$E_k = \tfrac{1}{2}mv^2$$

Here m is the mass of the body and v is the magnitude of its velocity. It can be shown from Newton's laws that the change in the kinetic energy of a body is equal to the work done on it.

What does the work? When a sliding or rolling body slows down, it loses kinetic energy; it does work against the force of friction. When a body falls toward the ground it gains kinetic energy. The work is done on the body by the force of gravity. If we lift a fallen body to its original height we have to do work, an amount of work equal to the kinetic energy it gained in falling. In lifting the body we give it *potential energy*. If it falls again, this energy is changed to kinetic energy.

When we draw a bow, we do work, which is stored in the bow as potential energy. When we release the string, the string does work on the arrow; the potential energy of the bow is gone and the arrow has an equal (for a 100%-efficient bow) amount of kinetic energy.

All this can be derived from Newton's laws of motion. It can be applied directly to the motions of electrons. We now know of many sorts of energy with which Newton was unfamiliar: thermal energy, electromagnetic energy, nuclear energy. The law of conservation of energy has been generalized to include them all. In reckoning up all the energy, kinetic energy and mechanical work still appear in their familiar forms. When an electron is accelerated, its kinetic energy, which is one half the product of its mass times the square of its velocity, increases. This increase is equal to the work done on the electron—the component of force acting in the direction of motion times the distance over which the electron moves while the force acts. To increase the kinetic energy, energy must be supplied from some source, though it be from a source that Newton never dreamed of.

Chapter Three

ELECTRIC FIELDS AND ELECTRONS

Ions and electrons are called *charged particles*: *particles* because they are small, and *charged* because an electron or an ion has an *electric charge*, a quantity of electricity, associated with it.

Two charged particles at rest act on each other with an inverse-square law of force just as do two gravitating masses. The differences are that the magnitude of the force is proportional to the product of the charges, not of the masses; that like charges (two positive charges or two negative charges) repel one another and unlike charges attract one another; and that electric forces are much stronger than gravitational forces.

The interaction of charges in motion and the way in which this interaction depends on the velocities of the charges are very complicated. Moreover, electrons, unlike planets, are far too numerous in practical devices for us to reckon their mutual interactions individually. How, then, are we to deal with the forces on electrons?

Michael Faraday, a great physicist of the nineteenth century, knew almost no mathematics. He was puzzled about the interaction of charges and of currents of electricity (particles of electricity such as electrons had not been discovered in his day). He sought some graphic way of representing the nature of the forces he found, and he hit on the idea of electric and magnetic fields, represented graphically by lines of force. To understand anything about electronics, we must understand something about electric and magnetic fields.

The Gravitational Field

Fields have become a prized and universal tool of physics. They can represent gravitational forces as well as electric forces. Because we already have discussed gravity, it will be easiest first to illustrate fields in the case of the gravitational field, and to see how the gravitational field is connected with Newton's inverse-square law of force.

We really define what we mean by a "gravitational field" by saying that in a gravitational field an object experiences a force. The magnitude of the force is given by the product of the strength of the field and the mass of the object. The direction of the force is given by the direction of the field.

The gravitational field of a single spherical body like the earth or the sun is everywhere directed toward the center of the sphere. The strength of the field is proportional to the mass of the body, m, and inversely proportional to the square of the distance from the center, r. Thus, the strength, F, of the gravitational field of mass m is written:

$$F = \frac{gm}{r^2}$$

We can, if we like, represent the field pictorially by drawing gravitational lines of force. These come in from infinity toward the center of the object, as shown in Fig. 10. Of course, the figure is a flat picture and shows the lines in one plane only, but we can imagine lines of force coming in from all directions, like the toothpicks stuck in a grapefruit to support canapes.

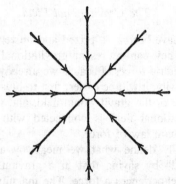

Figure 10

The gravitational field at any point is a vector; that is, it has direction and magnitude. We should not, however, confuse the lines of force with vectors just because I have put arrowheads on them in Fig. 10 to show their directions. The lines of force are merely a picture of the field. They may be, and usually are, curved, although they are straight in the simple case we have been discussing. The direction of the lines of force is at each point the direction of the field, which is a vector.

In Fig. 10, we can draw in as many lines of force as we wish. However, we will note that the lines of force get farther apart the farther away we go. Let us imagine a spherical surface a distance r from the center of the mass that produces the gravitational field and its lines of force. The area of the surface of the sphere is $4\pi r^2$, so we see that the number of lines of force which cross a given area—one square meter, or one square foot, or one square mile—is inversely proportional to the square of the radius. Thus, if four lines of force cross an area of a square mile at a distance of 10,000 miles from the center of the earth, one line of force will cross each square mile at a distance of 20,000 miles from the center of the earth, since the square of 10,000 divided by 20,000, that is $(10,000/20,000)^2$, is $\frac{1}{4}$.

Newton said that the gravitational force is directed toward the attracting mass and is inversely proportional to the square of the distance. His law means that gravitational force is directly proportional to the density of lines of force which is, in our picture, the number of lines of force crossing a unit area. Thus, our lines of force give a very complete picture of the gravitational field. Not only do they show the direction of the force it produces on masses, but their density gives the strength of the field, that is, the magnitude of the force.

What of the gravitational field of many objects? Like velocity, the gravitational field of a body at a given point has magnitude and direction, and we can represent it by an arrow or vector, just as we did velocity. For instance, suppose that in Fig. 11 the vector A represents the gravitational field of planet a at a given point, while B represents the gravitational field of planet b and C represents the gravitational field of planet c. The total gravitational field at the point is the vector-sum D of the individual

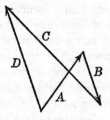

Figure 11

field vectors, *A*, *B*, and *C*. Thus, if we know the field at every point produced by the masses individually, we can get the total field at every point by vector addition.

While we can find the field produced by a number of bodies by adding vectorially the fields produced by each, this is impractical in many cases. Faraday showed that electric and magnetic fields obey certain general rules, however they are produced, and James Clerk Maxwell later expressed these mathematically in the wonderful equations which describe completely the behavior of electric and magnetic fields. We will encounter these in Chapter Six.

Nowadays we think of fields as things in themselves: their form is specified, and they fully represent the forces which bodies will encounter at various points in space. The lines of force of a complicated field may be very complicated curves, yet the strength of the field at any point is proportional to the density of lines of force at that point. Thus, the representation of a field by lines of force gives a striking picture of its properties.

Fields are very important to us, because it is in

terms of fields that the forces on electrons are expressed. Like skaters and planets, electrons obey Newton's laws of motion. When a force acts in the direction of motion of an electron, the electron speeds up; when a force acts against its direction of motion, it slows down; and when a force acts exactly normal to (perpendicular to, at right angles to) its direction of motion, the electron turns without changing speed.

The force acting on a skater may be a friendly push, a gust of wind, or the friction of his skates on the ice. The force acting on a star or on a planet is the gravitational attraction of other celestial bodies. From a slightly different point of view, we say that it is the force due to the gravitational field of these bodies.

Electrons are acted on by electric and magnetic fields. Electrons and currents of electrons produce electric and magnetic fields, and we express the forces that they exert on other electrons in terms of the fields themselves.

Electric Fields

Let us consider electric fields first, and leave magnetic fields until later. Electric fields are very closely akin to gravitational fields. The action of the electric field on an electron is analogous to that of a gravitational field on a mass. But, the direction of the force depends on whether the charge is positive or negative. An electric field pushes a negative charge in just exactly the opposite direction from that in which it pushes a positive charge. The direction of the electric field is defined as the direction in which it pushes a positive charge. Hence, an electron, which has a negative charge, is pushed just opposite to the direction of the electric field. However, when I put arrows on electric lines of force in this chapter these arrows will indicate the direction in which the electric field pushes an electron. The same field would push a positive particle, such as a proton or positron, in the opposite direction, which is truly the direction of the electric field. The magnitude of the force is given by the product of the strength of the electric field and the charge of the electron.

The astronomer who deals with gravitational fields is confronted with particular fields that already exist in a world he never made. His problem is to calculate the motions of heavenly bodies in these fields. The problem of the electronics engineer is quite different; it is to produce inside a vacuum tube fields which will cause electrons to go where he wants them to go and to do what he wants them to do. He is fundamentally a maker of universes, on a small scale of course, rather than a student of a universe already given.

The electronics engineer produces the electric fields he wants by applying a voltage between electrodes, that is, pieces of metal which conduct electricity.

A conductor is full of electrons which are free to move within the conductor but in general cannot escape through its surface because an electric field normal to the surface exists in an exceedingly thin region just inside the surface of the conductor. The inside of a conductor contains fixed positive charges equal in total charge to the charge of the free electrons. Suppose we tried to produce an electric field inside a conductor. If we succeeded in producing such a field, the field would cause the electrons in the conductor to move. They would move into such a pattern of charge that another field would be produced just canceling the field initially inside the conductor. Then there would be no cause for the electrons to move any more. When the field became zero the electrons would cease to move. Hence there is never any electric field inside a conductor.*

If we connect one electrode to the positive terminal of a battery and another electrode to the negative terminal of a battery, there will be an electric field between the two electrodes, and this field will exert a force on any electron in it. The general direction of the force will be away from the negative electrode and toward the positive electrode.

The field extends right up to the surface of the electrodes. A fundamental law of electric fields is that very near the surface of an electrode—that is, a conductor, any piece of metal—the direction of the electric field must be normal to the surface of the conductor. The electric field exerts a force on the electrons near the surface of the conductor. If the electric field is normal to the surface, this force is straight inward or outward. An outward force draws an excess of electrons to the surface. An inward force pushes the electrons in from the surface and leaves an excess of positive charges. If, however, there were

* This is strictly true only for perfect conductors. A feeble electric field can be maintained even in a good conductor like copper. Such a field causes a continual strong flow of electrons, that is, an electric current, through the material. The electrons heat the copper by continually bumping into imperfections, and electric energy must be supplied continually to maintain the field.

a component of the electric field parallel to the surface, it would cause the electrons to slide along parallel to the surface just inside the conductor, and this movement would rearrange the electrons and so change the electric field that it would become normal to the surface of the conductor at all points.

Thus, we have two important rules or laws concerning electric fields: (1) there is no electric field within a conductor; (2) the electric field just outside a conductor is always normal to the surface of the conductor.

Current Flow in a Diode

Let us consider the sort of conducting electrodes that may be used in a particular type of vacuum tube. The simplest form of vacuum tube is the *diode*. Fig. 12 shows the parts of a diode. The drawing does not resemble closely any practical diode that you will find in a TV set. Such a diode is very compactly made, and a drawing of it would be confusing.

The two electrodes of the diode are the *cathode* and the *anode*. In Fig. 12, the cathode is a sort of rectangular pipe or sleeve made of thin nickel and coated on the outside with a mixture of barium and strontium oxides. The purpose of the coating is to make it easy for electrons to leave the cathode when it is heated. The coating reduces the field just inside the surface that holds the electrons inside the conductor.

The cathode is heated by an internal electric heater of tungsten wire. In the drawing, power from battery B_1 heats the heater and the heater heats the cathode. When the cathode is hot, the electrons inside it

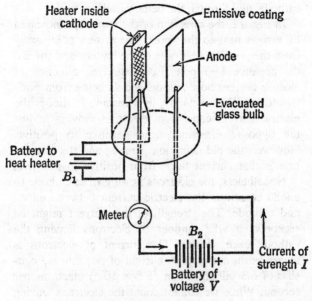

Heater inside cathode

Emissive coating

Anode

Evacuated glass bulb

Battery to heat heater

B_1

Meter

B_2

Current of strength I

Battery of voltage V

Figure 12

rush about with increased velocities, and some are able to pass through the surface of the cathode and into the vacuum inside the glass envelope.

The anode is simply a flat piece of metal. When the anode is connected to the positive terminal of a battery B_2 of voltage V whose negative terminal is connected to the cathode, there is an electric field between cathode and anode, and the electric field is such as to force electrons toward the anode. Thus, when the anode is positive with respect to the cathode, an electric current flows between anode and cathode and through the external circuit, that is, the wires connecting the battery to the anode and the cathode, and through the battery itself.

In Fig. 12, the direction of the current is indicated by arrows next to the wires. The arrows point away from the positive (+) pole of the battery and toward the negative (−) pole. Long ago, the direction of electric current flow was defined as being from positive to negative. Actually, in wires and in diodes the electric current consists of electrons moving in just the opposite direction, from negative to positive. However, the old definition persists, and the convention is that current flows from positive to negative.

Nonetheless, the electrons flowing from cathode to anode constitute the electric current between anode and cathode. The strength of this current might be reckoned by the number of electrons leaving the cathode each second. The current of electrons is measured in *amperes*. A current of one ampere consists of 6.3 billion billion (6.3×10^{18}) electrons per second. While we cannot count the electrons leaving the cathode and striking the anode, we can connect an *ammeter* (which measures amperes), a *milliammeter* (which measures thousandths of amperes) or a *microammeter* (which measures millionths of amperes) between the cathode and the negative terminal of the battery. Then, all the electrons emitted by the cathode, which are supplied to the cathode from the negative terminal of the battery, must pass through the meter. The meter in effect measures the number of electrons passing through it each second, reckoned in amperes, milliamperes (thousandths of an ampere) or microamperes (millionths of an ampere).

How much current flows when a given voltage, V,

is applied across the diode? If electrons are emitted copiously from the cathode, not all those emitted reach the anode, for as the negative electrons move out toward the anode they produce an electric field opposite to that produced by the positive anode, a field that tends to prevent electrons from leaving the cathode. The greater the applied voltage, the greater is the *space charge* needed to cancel the field it produces, and the greater the current will be. But the current will depend on the spacing between the cathode and anode, too. For a given voltage more current will flow per unit area of cathode if the spacing between cathode and anode is small, leaving little room for space charge.

Suppose we connect the battery between anode and cathode so that the anode is negative with respect to the cathode. No current will flow, because the field is such as to force electrons back toward the cathode. If, however, the battery is so connected that the anode is positive with respect to the cathode, then as we increase the battery voltage and make the anode more and more positive, more and more current will flow. If we plot current I vs. voltage V, the plot will look somewhat as shown in Fig. 13. This

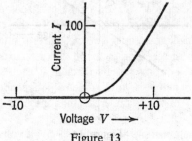

Figure 13

shows zero current at a voltage of -10 volts and a current of 100 milliamperes at a voltage of $+10$ volts.

Such a curved or *non-linear* relation between voltage and current is in contrast to the relation between voltage and current which is characteristic of imperfect conductors, or *resistors*, such as coils of fine wire or mixtures of carbon and non-conducting material. For such *linear* devices the plot of current I vs. voltage V is a straight line, as shown in Fig. 14. Mathematically, we can write:

$$V = IR, \qquad I = \frac{V}{R}$$

Here, R is a constant called the *resistance* of the device. This relation is called *Ohm's law*, and the unit of resistance is the *ohm*. If a coil of wire has a resistance of 10 ohms, and if we connect it to a battery with a voltage of 1 volt, a current of $\frac{1}{10}$ amperes will flow.

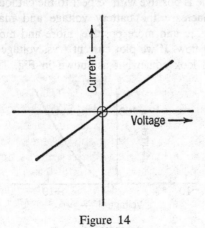

Figure 14

Diodes simply do not obey Ohm's law. Therein lies their value. They can be used in obtaining a *direct current* (a current which flows in one direction only) from an alternating voltage (one which is sometimes positive and sometimes negative). Also, the curved nature of the characteristic of the diode is valuable in changing a signal of one frequency to a signal of another frequency, as we shall see in Chapter Eight.

The Electron Gun

Essentially the same parts used in a diode appear in another important electronic device, the *electron gun*. Electron guns are used to produce beams of electrons in TV picture tubes, in amplifiers for radio signals of extremely high frequencies, and in many other devices.

Fig. 15 shows the electrodes of a simple electron gun. Here no attempt is made to show the parts in perspective or to include the evacuated envelope. The chief electrodes, E_1 and E_2, are two parallel sheets of metal, each with a central aperture. One of these is connected by a wire to the negative terminal of a battery (marked −) and the other is connected to the positive terminal of the battery (marked +). The electric lines of force between the two electrodes are shown as lines with arrowheads indicating the direction of the force the field produces on electrons. The lines of force must, as we have seen, be normal to the electrodes at the surface. In this case, the electric lines of force between the two parallel-plane electrodes are very simple. They are straight, parallel, and uniformly spaced except near the edges of the plates. The electric field between the two parallel-plane electrodes is everywhere the same in magnitude and direction.

In the electron gun of Fig. 15, a little metal cup with an electric heating coil inside acts as the cathode. This cathode is centered in the aperture in the negative electrode, and it is connected with a wire to the negative electrode E_1, and hence to the negative terminal of the battery.

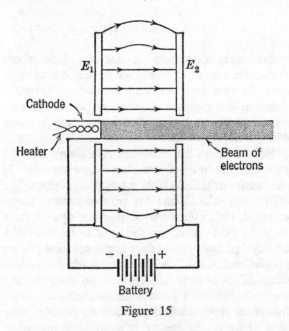

Figure 15

The electric field between the electrodes E_1 and E_2 accelerates the electrons to the right, so that a *beam* of electrons (by analogy with a beam of light) travels from the cathode toward the positive electrode E_2, which is the anode of the electron gun. This anode has a hole in it, toward which the electrons move. While there is a small electric field pushing the electrons toward the edge of the hole in the anode, this is insufficient to deflect them very much from their motion in a straight line; the electrons pass through the hole in the anode and travel on through the vacuum beyond to perform any of a variety of functions.

As in the simple diode, the current leaving the cathode is limited by the space charge of the electrons in the beam; the greater the voltage between cathode and anode, the greater the current flow. In some electron guns the electrode E_1 is not attached directly to the cathode, but a voltage V_1 is applied between it and the cathode. If E_1 is made negative with respect to the cathode, fewer electrons will leave the cathode. Thus, the voltage V_1 can be used to control the current of the electron beam produced by the gun.

An electron gun much like that of Fig. 15 may supply electrons to "illuminate" the specimen in an electron microscope and so enable a chemist or a biologist to see details far smaller than a wave of light, and scarcely larger than molecules. The electrodes of such a gun look somewhat as shown to the left in Fig. 16. The cathode is a mere hairpin of tungsten, heated by passing current through it as in the filament of an electric lamp, and the electrodes E_1 and E_2 have shapes somewhat different from those shown in Fig. 15. The electrons from an electron gun may travel from the gun in a beam in the picture tube of your television receiver and paint on the screen scenes of astounding variety. A somewhat

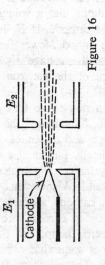
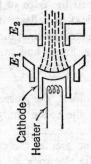

Figure 16

larger electron gun may supply the electron beam in a microwave amplifier tube, which amplifies television signals at relay points while sending them from coast to coast. Or it may be a part of a powerful amplifier for radar, which sends out radio pulses of millions of watts' power to locate or guide planes or missiles. Electron guns for such tubes look much as shown to the right in Fig. 16. The cathode is concave, and electrodes E_1 and E_2 being curved, the electric lines of force converge or draw closer together in going from E_1 to E_2. From this arrangement of electrodes, and the concave cathode, a converging beam of electrons results. Electron guns form a part of many other electronic devices besides electron microscopes, picture tubes, and microwave amplifiers.

The French call an electron gun a *canon électronique*. The energetic language does not mean, however, that French electron guns are of larger caliber than the American variety. Physically, they both come in various sizes. Some used in low-power microwave amplifiers have a cathode only a fiftieth of an inch in diameter. Those used in microwave amplifiers producing millions of watts of power have cathodes broader than one's hand. The electron gun in an electron microscope may furnish only microamperes. The electron gun in a powerful microwave amplifier for producing radar pulses may furnish beams of tens of amperes—millions of times as many electrons per second. For comparison, the electric current in the filament of a 100-watt light bulb is a little less than an ampere.

Deflection of Electron Beams

In the electron gun an electric field is used chiefly to increase the velocity of electrons, to speed them up. An electric field applied transverse to the direction of motion of electrons will change their direction of motion. For instance, in Fig. 17 a beam of

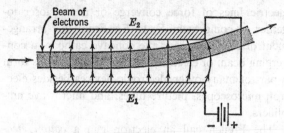

Figure 17

electrons passes between two parallel-plane electrodes, E_1 and E_2, and E_2 is held positive with respect to E_1 by means of a battery. The electric lines of force are about as indicated. As the electrons move from left to right, they are accelerated upward; the electron beam emerging at the right travels up at an angle, not horizontally. The electron beam has been *deflected* from its original direction.

Deflection is put to use in the cathode-ray oscilloscope tube, which displays variations of voltage with time in various electronic circuits. Fig. 18 shows the parts of a cathode-ray oscilloscope. A narrow electron beam from an electron gun is directed at the center of a *fluorescent screen*. This screen is a

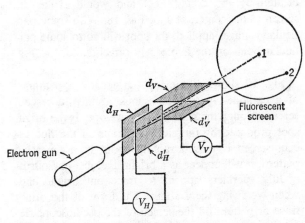

Figure 18

coating of some substance on the inside of the flat
end of a cone-shaped glass envelope which encloses
the gun and the other parts of the device. The coating, which is of the same sort of material used in
fluorescent lights, glows when the electrons of the
beam strike it, producing a bright spot of light.

Between the electron gun and the fluorescent
screen are two sets of deflection plates, the horizontal
deflection plates d_H and d'_H and the vertical deflection plates d_V and d'_V. A voltage V_H applied between d_H and d'_H deflects the beam sideways and
moves the spot left or right on the fluorescent screen.
A voltage V_V applied between d_V and d'_V deflects
the beam vertically and moves the spot up or down
on the fluorescent screen. If V_H and V_V were zero,
the beam would go straight through the tube, as in-

dicated by the dotted line, and would strike the screen at the center, at 1 of Fig. 18. With some particular voltages applied, the spot will go to some particular point on the fluorescent screen as to 2 in Fig. 18.

Fig. 19 shows at the top the general appearance of a cathode-ray tube. We look at the fluorescent screen through the glass of the envelope. If the bright spot produced by the electron beam on the fluorescent screen is moved rapidly about in a repeating pattern, it will appear as a bright line, just as Fourth-of-July sparklers appear to trace out bright lines when we swing them about. The form of the bright trace or pattern on the screen of the oscilloscope depends on the voltages applied to the deflecting plates.

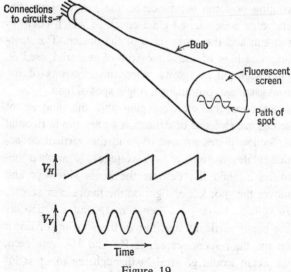

Figure 19

Commonly (but not always) the voltage applied to the deflecting plates which move the beam in a horizontal direction increases linearly with, or proportionally to, time; then the left-to-right motion of the beam measures out time. When the beam has gone clear across the screen, the voltage is changed to move it back to the left side of the screen. Again the voltage increases linearly with time and the beam travels from left to right, measuring out time evenly with distance. Such a voltage is shown as V_H in Fig. 19. In this case, whatever voltage V_V is applied to the plates to move the spot vertically will be mapped out faithfully as a function of time on the screen of the oscilloscope tube. For instance, if the voltage V_V varies sinusoidally with time, as shown in Fig. 19, a sine wave will appear on the face of the oscilloscope tube, as shown.

Oscilloscopes are invaluable tools for study of the behavior of electric circuits. They can be used to display phenomena which occur in a few billionths of a second. Electronic-research workers, design engineers and TV repairmen would all be helpless without oscilloscopes to map out for them the complicated behavior of the voltages in electronic devices.

Various electron tubes and other electronic devices make use of magnetic fields as well as electric fields. Before we go on to magnetic fields, however, it is wise to consider some fundamental matters concerned with electric fields; these are the relation between the flow of electrons between electrodes and the current in the wires connected to the electrodes, and the conservation of energy. These matters can be very complicated when the voltages applied to the electrodes change rapidly with time. We will not consider this difficult case. Matters are much simpler when the voltages are constant with time, or when they change negligibly in the time it takes an electron to get from one electrode to the other.

Electrostatic Fields and Conductors

Electrostatic fields are electric fields which do not change with time. Electrostatic fields have a particularly important property. When an electron travels between any two points in an electrostatic field, the work done on it is the same, regardless of the path, direct or indirect, by which the electron travels between the two points.

Let us now link this up with what we know about conductors. Consider two conductors or electrodes A and B connected to the negative and positive terminals of a battery, as shown in Fig. 20. From the property of electrostatic fields that we have stated, we can see that when an electron moves from *a particular point* in conductor A to *a particular point* in conductor B, the work that the electric field does on the electron will not depend on the path followed by the electron. But remember, there is no electric field inside a conductor. Hence, there is no force on an electron inside a conductor, and it takes no additional work to move an electron from any point inside conductor A to any other point inside conductor A, or from any point inside conductor B to any other point inside conductor B.

From this it follows that the same work is done on an electron by the electric field when the electron moves from any point on electrode A to any point on electrode B, regardless of just where the electron

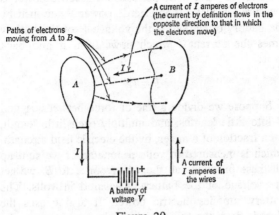

Paths of electrons moving from A to B

A current of I amperes of electrons (the current by definition flows in the opposite direction to that in which the electrons move)

A

B

I

A current of I amperes in the wires

A battery of voltage V

Figure 20

leaves or where it arrives or what path it follows. Thus, all electrons which leave electrode A at rest will have the same velocity and the same kinetic energy when they strike electrode B. Where does this energy come from?

The energy is supplied from the battery as electric power. If the flow of electrons between electrodes A and B constitutes a current of I amperes, a current of I amperes will flow from one terminal of the battery connecting the electrodes and back into the other, as shown in Fig. 20. We should remember that, by a definition made long before electrons were discovered, the current flows in a direction opposite to that of electron flow. In Fig. 20, the small arrowheads on the electron paths from A to B indicate direction of electron motion and the large-headed arrows indicate current flow.

Power is work done per second. Electric power is measured in watts. The electric power P supplied by the battery of Fig. 20 is the voltage V of the battery times the current I which flows from it and back to it:

$$P = IV$$

Suppose we divide a line of force between A and B into little lengths, and multiply each little length, each fraction of a meter, by the electric field strength, which is measured in volts per meter. If we sum up all these products, all the way from A to B, we get the voltage of the battery, measured in volts. The battery supplies electric power. It also causes the electric field, the field which produces a force on the electrons between electrodes A and B and gives the electrons kinetic energy. The conversion of electric power from batteries or other electric generators into kinetic energy of electrons is a process we encounter over and over again in electron devices. In these, as in the whole universe, the books always balance. The electric energy that disappears from the electric generator (the battery, in this case) all reappears as kinetic energy of accelerated electrons.

Chapter Four

MAGNETIC FIELDS, TOO

While in some ways electric fields are more important in vacuum tubes than are magnetic fields, many tubes require both for their operation. Indeed, we will find out in Chapter Six that electric and magnetic fields are so closely related that when we have one we usually have a certain amount of the other. However, the ways in which the fields are produced and the ways in which they act on electrons are quite distinct.

We have seen that electric fields are associated with electric charges, and are produced usually by applying a voltage to a pair of electrodes, as by means of a battery. There are no magnetic charges or isolated *poles*. There is no analogue of a magnetic battery. An electric battery can cause a flow of electric charges; an electric battery changes chemical energy into electric energy. There are no magnetic charges to flow.

Magnetic fields can be produced by permanent magnets, but often they are produced by an electric current, that is, a flow of electrons, through a coil of copper wire. A coil of wire connected to the terminals of a battery as shown in Fig. 21 produces a magnetic field inside the coil in the direction shown. The arrows beside the wire show the direction of

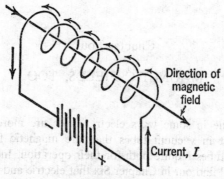

Figure 21

current flow, which is from the positive terminal of the battery, through the coil, and back to the negative terminal.

We know that what is actually flowing in the wires is electrons and that these move through the wire from the negative terminal of the battery to the positive terminal. We should remember that a direction of current flow was defined long before anyone knew about electrons, and that the direction of current flow is contrary to the direction of electron flow.

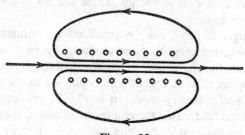

Figure 22

We can draw the coil of Fig. 21 in cross section and show the lines of force, as in Fig. 22. Inside the coil, or *solenoid*, the magnetic lines of force are nearly parallel, and the strength of the field is thus very nearly constant. Hence, we can use such a solenoid to produce a uniform magnetic field.

More often, we use an electromagnet with a *core* of iron or, often, of an iron alloy with desirable magnetic properties. Such an electromagnet for producing a uniform magnetic field is shown in Fig. 23. The magnetic lines of force which stray far out in the solenoid of Fig. 22 are confined to the iron in the

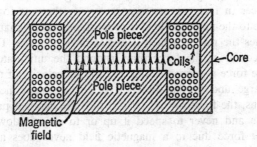

Figure 23

electromagnet of Fig. 23, and a very strong magnetic field appears between two projecting portions of the core called *pole pieces*.

The Force of a Magnetic Field

If there were isolated magnetic poles, as Ehrenhaft tried to persuade us a few years ago, a magnetic field would exert a force on them in the direction of the magnetic lines of force. Actually, there are no isolated magnetic poles. In describing a magnetic field we use lines of force, just as for an electric field, and the field is strongest where the lines of force are crowded closest together. However, a magnetic field produces a force on a charge only when the charge is moving. The magnitude of the force is proportional to the product of the magnetic field strength, the charge, and the component of the charge's velocity normal to the magnetic field. Thus, if a charge moves parallel to the magnetic lines of force, the magnetic field produces no force on it, while for a given speed the maximum force is produced if the charge moves normal (perpendicular) to the magnetic lines of force. In fact, we can accurately say that the force due to the magnetic field is proportional to the charge times the rate at which it passes lines of force. The direction of the force may astound the uninitiated. The force is perpendicular to both the velocity of the charge and to the direction of the magnetic field. Thus, the force always acts to turn the charged particle and never to speed it up or to slow it down. The force due to a magnetic field never does any work on a moving charge.

We may express the magnitude of the force F acting on a charged particle moving in a magnetic field by

$$F = q\mu H v_n$$

Here q is the electric charge of the particle, μ (mu) is a constant called the permeability of space, H is the magnetic field strength, and v_n is the component of velocity normal to the magnetic field.

Let us imagine that we have a uniform magnetic field of strength H such as might be produced by the electromagnet of Fig. 23. Suppose we set a charged particle in motion with a velocity v in a horizontal plane, normal to the lines of force. What will the motion of the particle be?

Since the force of the magnetic field is normal to the velocity, the particle will be neither speeded up nor slowed down. It will be acted on by a constant force,

$$q\mu Hv,$$

normal to the direction of motion. It will turn at a constant rate; it will travel in a circle.

How long will it take the particle to go once around the circle? We have seen in Chapter Two that the acceleration a of an object traveling in a circle is:

$$a = \frac{2\pi v}{T}$$

From Newton's second law, the mass m times the acceleration must be equal to the force acting on the particle. That is,

$$\frac{m2\pi v}{T} = q\mu Hv$$

As v appears as a factor on each side, we see that the period does not depend on the velocity. In fact, we see that

$$T = \frac{2\pi}{\mu H(q/m)}$$

Thus, in a uniform magnetic field charged particles go around in circles with a constant period T. The radius of the circle depends on the velocity. The circumference of a circle of radius r is $2\pi r$, so we must have

$$v = \frac{2\pi r}{T}$$

and

$$r = \frac{T}{2\pi} v$$

The Cyclotron

If we were able to increase the speed of a charged particle circling in a uniform magnetic field, the period would remain constant but the particle would swing around in larger and larger circles. This is just what happens in the *cyclotron*, a device used for accelerating positive ions to atom-smashing speeds.

In a cyclotron, a flat, pillbox-shaped vacuum chamber is located between the poles of a powerful magnet such as that of Fig. 23. Inside the chamber is a pair of dees (named from the shape), as shown at the top of Fig. 24. The ions travel around between the dees. An accelerating voltage, V, which varies periodically with time as shown at the bottom of Fig. 24, is applied between the dees. This voltage changes from positive to negative to positive again in just the time it takes the ion to circle once between the dees. Thus, if the second dee is negative with respect to the first as a positive ion passes between the two at A, so that the ion will be accelerated, then when the same ion reaches B the first dee will be negative with respect to the second and the ion will be accelerated again. Thus, the ion will spiral outward as shown.

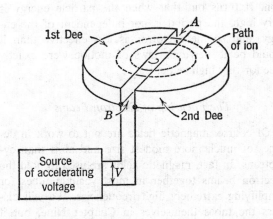

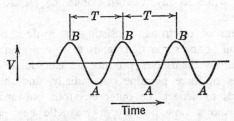

Figure 24

Out at the edge of the dees, an aperture is provided, and a strong electric field deflects the ions out of the cyclotron at that particular point.

Cyclotrons with diameters as great as 17 feet have been made. Such a huge beast will accelerate particles to energies of almost half a billion volts (that is, to the velocity that would be given by a battery of that voltage). In such devices, Newton's laws of motion are in error. To describe their operation accurately, one must use *relativistic* equations of motion. It turns out that when the particle energy is very high, the period is not independent of the energy, and so the cyclotron is less effective than it would be if Newton's laws of motion were exactly true for very high velocities.

The Focusing of Electron Beams

Of course, magnetic fields are put to work in devices of much more modest size and aims than cyclotrons. In fact, magnetic fields are used to hold the electron beams together in most vacuum tubes for amplifying extremely high frequencies. We will discuss the tubes themselves in Chapter Nine, but it is worth while to say a word about the electron beams here.

A beam of electrons, consisting as it does of charges all of the same sign, tends to spread apart. The electrons themselves produce an electric field with lines of force pointing out radially, and this field tends to deflect the outer electrons outward. Fig. 25 shows how a uniform magnetic field is used to hold a beam of electrons together.

The uniform field extends from a flat iron pole piece to another pole piece located somewhere to the right. The electron beam enters the field through a hole through the pole piece. Near the hole the lines of force spread out as shown, and some of them terminate on the inside of the hole through the pole piece. Thus, as the electrons of the beam go through the hole they must cross a radial component of magnetic field. This component produces a force directed around the axis of the hole and sets the electrons whirling around the axis. Now, because of this mo-

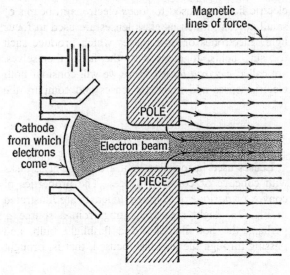

Figure 25

tion about the axis, the electrons have a component of velocity normal to the parallel lines of magnetic force in the main, uniform portion of the magnetic field. As the electrons move across the parallel lines of force, the magnetic field produces a constant inward force on them. If the magnetic field has just the right strength, and if the electrons enter it parallel, the force will be just right to overcome the outward force due to the electric field produced by the electrons in the beam, and the beam diameter will remain constant as the electrons travel in helical paths through the magnetic field.

Magnetic fields are used to confine electron beams as in Fig. 25 only in amplifier tubes, where beam currents are fairly large. However, both magnetic and electric fields are used to *focus* electrons in beams of small current, much as glass lenses are used to focus light. Electrodes or pole pieces which produce such focusing fields, together with the fields themselves, are called *electron lenses*. Here we will consider both electric lenses and magnetic lenses and compare the two.

Electric Lenses

Lenses used in focusing light are round glass disks with concave or convex surfaces. The properties of convex or *positive* or *converging* lenses are illustrated in Fig. 26. Light rays emanating from a source *a*, perhaps the hot filament of a flashlight bulb, and passing through the lens are focused, that is, brought

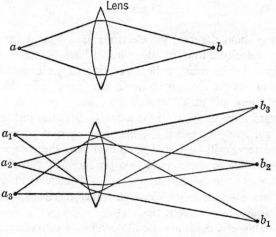

Figure 26

together, by the lens at some point, b. Suppose light leaves several points the same distance to the left of the lense; such points as a_1, a_2, a_3 in Fig. 26. The lens will bring the light from these points to a focus at 3 points, b_1, b_2, b_3 which are all at the same distance to the right of the lens. Thus, the lens forms an *image* of points a_1, a_2, and a_3.

We might replace the source of light a_1, a_2, a_3 by an illuminated object, such as a slide in a projector. Where the image falls at b_1, b_2, b_3 we could put a white screen and see the slide projected. Or a_1, a_2, a_3 might be stars, and b_1, b_2, b_3 the images of stars, to fall on a photographic plate or to be examined with the eyepiece of a telescope. Or a_1, a_2, a_3 might represent light coming from the illuminated specimen of a microscope, and b_1, b_2, b_3 parts of the image, again either to fall on a photographic plate or to be examined with an eyepiece.

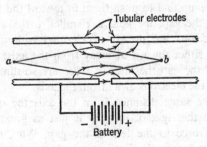

Figure 27

An *electron lens* focuses the paths of electrons just as a glass lens focuses rays of light. A typical electron lens consists of two coaxial metal tubes with a short gap between the ends, as shown in Fig. 27. The lines of force of the electric field are shown, with arrow-heads to point the direction of force on the electrons. The field is strongest near the short gap between the ends of the two tubes. It is weaker at the center of the tube, where its direction is entirely horizontal—that is, parallel to the axis of the tubes. The field dies away rapidly to the left and to the right of the gap.

Two typical electron paths show what happens to electrons which leave a point *a* at different angles and go through the electron lens. They are *focused* and brought together at a common point *b*. So (disregarding aberrations or imperfections in focusing) are any other electrons going through the electron lens from point *a*; all are brought to a focus at point *b*.

How does this come to be? Let us go along the electron path from *a* to *b*. As we approach the gap, the electrons cross the electric lines of force; as we can see, these are so directed as both to speed the electrons up and to push them in toward the axis. In passing the gap, the field is parallel to the axis and the electrons are merely accelerated without being pushed either toward or away from the axis. To the right of the gap the lines of force are so directed as to push the electrons away from the axis.

At the same distance from the axis the outward force to the right of the gap is just as great as the inward force to the left of the gap. Why, then, is there a net overall effect of pushing the electrons toward the axis, as shown by the electron paths or trajectories in Fig. 27? There are two reasons: First, change of velocity is proportional to force times time. The electrons are accelerated, speeded up, in passing the gap; they are going faster in passing through the outward-directed field to the right than they are in passing through the inward-directed field to the left. Thus, the outward-directed field has less time to act on the electrons than does the inward-directed field, and produces less change in velocity. The second reason depends on the fact that the inward-directed and outward-directed fields are stronger the farther we go from the axis. The paths are such that the electrons are farther from the axis to the left of the gap than to the right; hence, *along the actual path* the inward-directed force to the left of the gap is greater than the outward-directed force to the right.

If we consider what happens to an electron moving from *b* toward *a*, we see that the electron paths are the same for the electron traveling in either direction. In either case, the system of two tubes with an applied voltage acts as does a converging or convex lens for light, like a magnifying glass, a burning glass, or a camera lens. Electron lenses are always converging lenses, and there is no analogue of the concave lens, such as the eyepiece of an opera glass.

Magnetic Lenses

Magnetic fields also can be used to produce electron lenses, just as electric fields can. The configuration of the magnetic lines of force is like that of the electric lines of force of the electric electron lens of Fig. 25. To produce such a magnetic field, two tubular iron pole pieces are used, separated by a short gap. In the electric lens the electric field between the electrodes was obtained by connecting the electrodes to the terminals of a battery. In the magnetic lens the magnetic field is produced by current flowing through a coil wound around the hollow pole pieces, as shown in the cutaway view of Fig. 28. The coil is surrounded by an iron shell which connects the pole pieces outside of the coil.

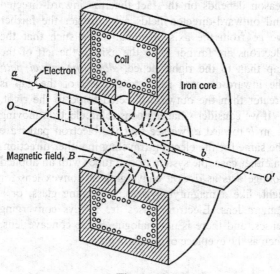

Figure 28

While the magnetic lines of force of the magnetic lens are much like the electric lines of force in the electric lens, the way in which they affect the electrons is quite different. The electron path between a and b in Fig. 28 illustrates the difference. As the electron approaches the gap between the pole pieces, it cuts lines of force which go from the inside of the tubular pole piece toward the axis; a force is produced normal to the magnetic lines of force, and this force starts the electron rotating clockwise about the axis. As the electron rotates about the axis it cuts the longitudinal lines of force near the center of the lens, and a resulting inward force pushes the electron in toward the axis. The electron then passes through the magnetic field beyond the gap where the lines of force are headed outward toward the inside of the pole piece. In cutting these lines of force the rotation of the electron about the axis is stopped. It is the inward push on the rotating electron near the center of the lens which is responsible for the focusing action of the magnetic lens.

Like electric electron lenses, magnetic electron lenses are very poor compared with the glass lenses used to focus light. Nonetheless, both electric and magnetic lenses are used in various important electronic devices.

Electric lenses are used in conjunction with electron guns in cathode-ray oscilloscope tubes such as that described in Chapter Three. An electron lens focuses the beam on the fluorescent screen to form the fine spot which writes out the pattern.

The picture tube of the TV receiver is a close relative of the oscilloscope tube, but the picture tube usually has a magnetic lens. The electron beam is deflected by transverse magnetic fields produced by an electromagnet structure called a *deflection yoke*. Fig. 29 shows the principal parts of a picture tube. An electron gun produces a beam of electrons which is sharply focused into a spot on a fluorescent screen. In order to form the picture, the spot is swept back and forth across the fluorescent screen, painting out the picture a line at a time. As the electron beam is swept across the screen the beam current, and hence the brightness of the spot, is controlled by a voltage

applied to an apertured electrode near the cathode of
the electron gun.

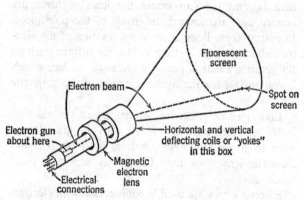

Figure 29

The Electron Microscope

The electron microscope is a powerful tool, useful
in research and in much routine medical and engineering work. It is superior to a light microscope because
it will disclose finer details. Electron microscopes
usually make use of magnetic lenses. If powerful electric lenses were used, it would be necessary to apply
a high voltage between the electrodes of the lenses,
and sparks or arcs might occur between the electrodes,
which would damage them. There is no such danger
with magnetic lenses.

Fig. 30 shows the essential parts of an electron
microscope without showing the vacuum-tight casing
which goes around the parts. To the left the equiva-

lent optical lenses are arrayed as they might be used in an optical microscope of similar function. In the optical microscope, there is a light source at the top. Next down is a convex *condenser lens*, which concentrates the light on the specimen below it. Just below the specimen is a powerful convex *objective lens*,

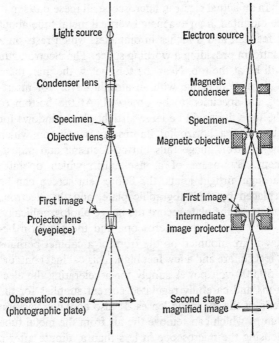

Light source

Electron source

Condenser lens

Magnetic condenser

Specimen

Specimen

Objective lens

Magnetic objective

First image

First image

Projector lens (eyepiece)

Intermediate image projector

Observation screen (photographic plate)

Second stage magnified image

Figure 30

which forms an image of the specimen, a first image, some distance below it. Just below the plane of the first image is a *projector lens*, which casts a magnified image of the first image on a photographic plate below. In the electron microscope to the right, an electron gun illuminates the specimen with electrons, as the light source in an optical instrument would illuminate it with light. Otherwise, the parts of the electron microscope are exactly analogous to those of the optical structure just described.

In an actual electron microscope all these parts may be mounted in an evacuated vertical metal tube about 3 feet tall and 8 inches in diameter, which rests on a platform providing a working space. The electron gun will be at the top. Near the top, below the gun, there will be an opening, with an airtight cover, for inserting the specimen to be observed. At the bottom of the tube there will be large airtight glass windows for observing a horizontal fluorescent screen on which the electron image falls during focusing and adjustment. By means of a mechanism which operates through airtight joints, the fluorescent screen can be replaced by a photographic plate, and the electrons falling on the plate record the image photographically.

The tube of the microscope and the platform below it are mounted on the front of a cabinet perhaps 2 feet square and a few feet high. This cabinet contains a 50,000-volt power supply for accelerating the electrons and carefully regulated current supplies for the coils of the magnetic lenses. It also contains vacuum pumps which can remove the air from the metal tube housing the microscope in less than a minute after a specimen has been inserted or a photographic plate changed.

Electron microscopes may magnify objects hundreds of thousands of times and show details as fine as a hundred-millionth of an inch. An ordinary light microscope can reveal details down to only about a hundred-thousandth of an inch. We will see in Chapter Five why this is so.

We have now explored many of the things we need to keep in mind in understanding electronics and electronic devices. We have encountered electric fields. There is an electric field at a point if a fixed charge experiences a force. The magnitude and the direction of the force give the magnitude and direction of the electric field. We can draw a picture which represents an electric field in terms of lines of force which are everywhere in the direction of the field, and whose density or closeness is proportional to the strength of the field. Electric fields are produced by applying a voltage between electrodes. The lines of force are everywhere normal to the surface of the electrodes. Electric fields can speed up charges, doing work on them.

Magnetic fields can be produced by the flow of electric current, as in coils. We can represent magnetic fields by lines of force. Magnetic fields, however, produce a force on moving charges only. The force is always normal, not only to the direction of the field, but also to the direction of motion of the electron. There is no component of force in the direction of motion. Magnetic fields cannot change the speed of an electron; they merely turn it in its path. Magnetic fields cannot do work on electrons.

These are matters to keep in mind for the discussions to follow.

Chapter Five

WAVES

There are some concepts so general and so far-reaching that they give us important information even about things whose precise physical nature is not well understood. Greatest of these concepts certainly is that of number. We know that two pigs and two pigs are four pigs, just as two men and two men are four men, or two canoes and two canoes are four canoes. The ideas of counting, of numbers, and of the correspondence between numbers and groups of objects apply to all distinct, relatively permanent things and collections of things, regardless of the nature of the objects.

Should we take this for granted? I have been told that there are primitive tribes which have words for one man, two men, three men, or many men, and quite separate words for one dog, two dogs, three dogs, and many dogs. Indeed, something of this attitude may survive in the engaging terms of venery: a gaggle of geese, a pride of lions, an ostentation of peafowl, and the rest.

Among the greatest of the great unifying concepts of physics is the idea of waves. Men must have observed waves from the earliest times. In the fifteenth century, Leonardo da Vinci wrote of waves, "The impetus is much quicker than the water, for it often happens that the wave flees the place of its creation, while the water does not; like the waves made in a field of grain by the wind, where we see the waves running across the field while the grain remains in place." Clearly, Leonardo recognized that when a wave of water moves from one place to another the water does not go bodily with it.

Modern physics is full of waves: the earthquake waves which seismologists study; the waves and ripples on oceans, lakes and ponds, the waves of sound which travel through the air; the mechanical waves in stretched strings and in the quartz crystals which are used to control the frequency of radio transmitters; the electromagnetic waves which constitute light, and which are radiated by radio transmitters and received by radio receivers; and finally, the waves of what?—probability, perhaps—which are used in quantum mechanics to predict the behavior of electrons, atoms, and complex substances.

What are waves? They are not earth, or water, or air; steel, or catgut, or quartz; yet they travel in these substances. Nineteenth-century physicists felt constrained to fill the vacuum of space with an *ether* to transmit electromagnetic waves, yet so arbitrary a substance seems more a placebo to quiet the disturbed mind than a valid explanation of a physical phenomenon. When we come to the waves of quantum mechanics, the physicists do not even offer us a single agreed-upon physical interpretation of the waves with which they deal, although they all agree in the way they use them to predict correctly the outcome of experiments.

The Principles of Wave Behavior

Rather than asking what waves are, we should perhaps ask, what can one say about waves? Here there is no confusion. One recognizes in waves a certain sort of behavior which can be described mathematically in common terms, however various may be the physical systems to which the terms are applied. Once we recognize that in a certain phenomenon we are dealing with waves, we can assert and predict a great deal about the phenomenon even though we do not clearly understand the mechanism by which the waves are generated and transmitted. The wave nature of light was understood, and many of its important consequences were worked out, long before the idea of an electromagnetic wave through space was dreamed of. Indeed, when the true explanation of the physical nature of light was proposed, many physicists who recognized clearly that light was some sort of wave refused to accept it.

We can study the important principles of waves in simple and familiar examples. As we come to understand the behavior of these waves, we can abstract certain ideas which are valid in connection with all waves, wherever we may find them. Such a study is the purpose of this chapter.

Suppose that we watch the waves of the sea from a pier. Let us imagine that today the waves are particularly smooth and are very regular in height. We see a certain number of crests pass us each second— let us say a number f. This number f is the *frequency* of the waves. Frequency is reckoned in *cycles per second*, or *cycles* for short. The cycle referred to is simply a complete cycle of change; the departing of a wave crest, the passing of the trough, and finally the arrival of the next crest. As a complete wave, from crest through trough to crest again, passes us, the height of the water goes through a complete cycle of change, from high to low to high again.

A cycle is a complete cycle of change, at the end of which we are back to the original state. It is the same in the case of 60-cycle electric power. The 60-cycle electric current alternates in direction of flow and goes through a complete cycle of change 60 times a second. Broadcast waves reach your receiver about a million crests a second; some television waves, a hundred million crests a second; and radar waves leave the radar antenna and are reflected back again at a rate of billions of waves or cycles per second.

Each wave in the ocean takes several seconds to pass us; thus the frequency of the ocean waves is a fraction of a cycle per second. We can measure, instead of the frequency, the time between the passing of two crests; this is the *period* of the wave, which we will call T. We see that T is the *reciprocal* of f, that is,

$$T = \frac{1}{f}$$

Looking out at the waves, we may estimate or measure the distance between the crests of the waves; this is the wavelength, which is always denoted by the Greek letter λ (lambda). Among radio waves, from radar to broadcast, the wavelength ranges from a little over an inch to around 1000 feet.

The time between the passage of wave crests is T. In this time the next crest must travel just one wavelength, λ, to reach the position of the preceding crest.

Thus, the wave travels with a velocity v which is the distance of travel, λ, divided by the elapsed time, T, so that

$$v = \frac{\lambda}{T} = \lambda f$$

Thus, we can express λ in terms of f and f in terms of λ by using the velocity, v:

$$\lambda = \frac{v}{f}$$

$$f = \frac{v}{\lambda}$$

Light waves and radio waves are both electromagnetic waves, and for such electromagnetic waves traveling through space, the velocity, v, is the velocity of light:

$$v = 186,000 \text{ miles per second}$$
$$v = 3 \times 10^8 \text{ meters per second}$$

Waves may have various shapes. We have been considering smooth rollers which come in one after another, regularly spaced. We can also have a single wave or a short *train* or waves such as those caused by throwing a single stone into a pond. There is a reason, however, for considering a particular regular, smooth, persistent kind of wave called a *sinusoidal* wave.

The waves we consider are waves of what is called *linear* systems. We will see what this means later on. Now, we will say merely that while for some linear systems a wave of any form travels along preserving that same form, in many other linear systems a wave of arbitrary form will change form as it travels. Consider, however, a wave such that, as it passes a given point, the height of the water or the magnitude or *amplitude* of some other significant quantity varies *sinusoidally* with time with some frequency *f*. If this is so at any point in any linear system, the wave will also vary sinusoidally with time, with the same frequency *f*, at any other point. Strictly, the term frequency should be applied to sine waves only.

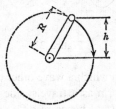

Figure 31

A sinusoidal variation can be understood in terms of a crank on a shaft which rotates at a constant rate, *f* turns per second, as shown in Fig. 31. The height, *h*, of the end of the crank above the level of center of the shaft (*h* is negative when the crank is below the shaft) varies sinusoidally with time. Mathematically, we express this by the equation

$$h = R \sin(2\pi f T)$$

Here *R* is the distance from the center of the shaft to the center of the crank, that is, the radius of the circle which the crank traces out. $sin(2\pi f T)$ stands for a particular function of the quantity $2\pi f T$, which is called the sine of that quantity. If we plot height or amplitude vs. time in seconds, as in Fig. 32, we get a *sine curve* or *sine wave*. This is the way the waves we will talk about vary with time. As long as the wave travels with a constant velocity, this is also the way the height above the mean or zero level, which is called the *amplitude*, varies with distance.

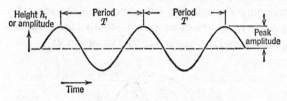

Figure 32

In instances in which a wave other than a sine wave will change in form as it travels, sine waves of different frequencies (and hence of different wavelengths) travel with different velocities. Henceforward, unless we say otherwise, we will mean a sine wave of some particular frequency when we speak of a wave, and the wave velocity will refer to the velocity of a sine wave of a particular frequency.

Let us think back to the waves that we watch from a pier in the ocean, and think of them as being sine waves. Imagine that they roll past a single pile sticking up from the water. The waves are very long compared with the diameter of the pile. We can imagine the water rising smoothly up the height of the pile and sinking smoothly down again, the height varying sinusoidally with time as the wave passes. Does the pile disturb or scatter the wave? Scarcely at all; a very little, perhaps. Here we have a fundamental rule concerning waves. They go right past objects small compared with the wavelength. The individual molecules of air are so small compared with light waves that they do not appreciably scatter the light waves. The droplets of fog, which are larger, scatter light waves but do not affect the short radio waves of radar. Rain drops will scatter short radar waves but do not affect waves of broadcast wavelength.

Obstacles can stop waves, however. Visualize a long breakwater extending parallel to the shore. Behind it, well away from the ends, the sea will be calm. Near one end, the waves will in effect bend around and get behind the breakwater a little. If we liken the waves of the ocean to light waves, and say by analogy that the shore is illuminated by the waves where the waves fall on it, then the breakwater casts a shadow on the shore. The shadow is not sharp, however; it is diffuse near the ends of the breakwater. The water near the shore passes gradually from calm to rough as we travel along the shore and pass one end of the breakwater.

It takes little to convince us that the sharpness of the shadow is connected with the length of the waves, and it indeed turns out that the length of the region between calm and rough, light and shade, is directly proportional to wavelength.

The great Newton did not accept the wave theory of light because light casts sharp shadows, and waves which he observed, such as waves of sound, do not. He was deceived, for optical shadows are so sharp merely because light waves are so short (they are around 20 millionths of an inch long). If one looks closely, however, one can see the diffuseness of shadows which is associated with the wave nature of light.

The Linearity of Waves

Can we understand the "shadows" cast by light more quantitatively? We can, and quite simply, too. In doing this, we must make use of the property of linearity of the waves which I have spoken of.

In order to explain linearity in a simple case, let us imagine that apples sold always for 5 cents each. Then, if we had 100 apples, we would know the total cost: 500 cents. We could if we wished point out any 10 apples and say those 10 apples cost 50 cents and all the rest together cost 450 cents. There is in this case a *linear* relation between the cost and the number of apples. The word linear is used because if we plotted cost of apples vs. number of apples, we would get a straight line.

If, however, apples were 5 cents for one and 6 for a quarter, we could make no such sweeping statements about a collection of 100 apples. We could not even say what the 100 apples cost, unless we knew the details of the transactions in which they were bought.

Linearity is a tremendously important concept in physics. We can say a great deal about linear systems. We know how to handle them mathematically. Nonlinear systems comprise that overwhelming majority of all systems. We can deal much less effectively with this huge variety of systems. Alas, most actual devices are more or less non-linear. It seems great good fortune that sound waves of ordinary amplitudes are linear, and that electromagnetic waves, embracing light and radio waves, are exactly linear.

It was because velocities add linearly that we could

break up the velocity vector into two components. It was because the force on a body attracted by two other bodies is the linear vector-sum of the attractions taken separately that we could represent the overall action by a field which is the sum of the fields of the individual bodies. It is because of this linearity that we could represent electric and magnetic fields by components, and the total field by the sum of the components. We can also represent waves in linear systems as a sum of components.

For instance, consider the small ripples on the surface of a pond which are caused by dropping a pebble into it. These ripples go out in concentric circles. If we simultaneously drop another pebble near by in the pond, the circular ripples or waves from it will pass right through the waves caused by the first pebble. If we concentrate our attention on the waves from either, we will see them as a simple circular pattern, undisturbed by the presence of the other pattern. If we look at the waves due to both pebbles, we will see them as a more complicated pattern, but everywhere the amplitude of this pattern, the height of the water, that is, is just the sum of the heights of the two circular patterns.

This sort of behavior is unusual in our world. If we fired two charges of shot through the same space, each load would pass through the other undisturbed only if the pellets were spaced very far apart, and even then not with certainty. We can imagine an even more striking example of a non-linear system. Imagine walking between a target and a gun. Imagine, separately, firing the gun at the target. Now imagine doing both simultaneously, so that the bullet hits you. It would not only be untrue, it would be meaningless to say that the result was the sum of the two separate acts. This example is extreme, perhaps, but it is not ridiculous; it merely shows how truly extraordinary linearity is in our world.

If we consider again the linear behavior of the pattern of ripples caused by the two pebbles dropped into the pond, we may well ask, what is the *true* pattern? Is it the sum of the two circular patterns? Is it the one complicated pattern? In the case of a linear system the question is meaningless. It is like asking, concerning 100 apples each of which was bought for 5 cents, whether the cost is 500 cents per hundred apples or 50 cents for each 10 apples. It is either and both. It is like asking whether a velocity is the single vector, v, or the sum of the horizontal component of velocity v_x, and the vertical component of velocity, v_y. The two components are merely an alternative way of representing the velocity, v.

Linearity makes it possible for us to talk of a complicated wave as the sum of a number of simpler component waves. This is not a matter of mere philosophical interest. It is a matter of the greatest practical significance.

Let us approach this problem by considering the pattern of two wave sources, from each of which concentric circles of sinusoidal waves travel out, with the same frequency, f, and the same velocity, v. I have tried to show a snapshot of this, a picture at one instant of time, in Fig. 33. Because it is hard to show sine waves, I have surrounded each of the sources, S_1 and S_2, with concentric rings of equal width, alternately blank and filled in with parallel lines. A blank circle plus a lined circle is one wavelength. I

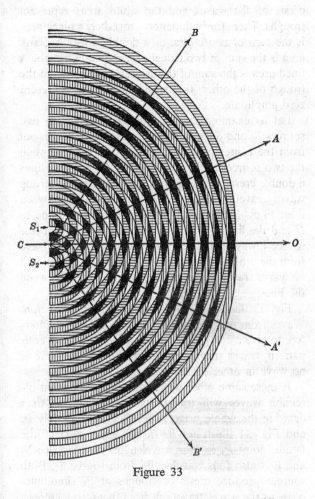

Figure 33

have drawn the lines of the lined circles at different angles for the circles from the two sources.

Let us imagine that the lined areas represent the

crests of the waves and the white areas represent troughs. Then, for both patterns together, a black area is the sum of two crests, or a double crest. A blank area is the sum of two troughs, or a double trough. A lined area is the sum of the crest of one wave and the trough of the other; that is, the lined areas represent zero amplitude.

Let us examine the total pattern due to the two sources S_1 and S_2. Look at the radial lines drawn out from the center point, C, which is midway between the two sources to O, A, A', B, B'. Along these lines a double crest alternates with a double trough. Strong waves travel in these directions. Midway between these lines—for instance, midway between the line to O and the line to A—the crest of the wave from one source always coincides with the trough of the wave from the other source; the total amplitude is zero, and no waves travel out in the directions midway between the lines.

Fig. 33 illustrates *wave interference* or *diffraction*. Waves from two sources of the same frequency *interfere* to give a complicated pattern, and, in the overall pattern, waves travel in some directions and there is no wave in other directions.

Is there some other way of finding out in what direction waves will travel, some way simpler than drawing the whole wave pattern? There certainly is, and Fig. 34 illustrates it. In the upper part of the figure, point P_1 is four wavelengths from source S_1 and it is also four wavelengths from source S_2. Both sources produce crests or troughs at P_1 simultaneously as the waves travel out from them, so the crests and troughs add up and there is a strong wave at P_1. In the lower part of Fig. 34, point P_2 is three and

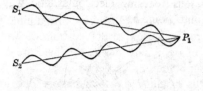

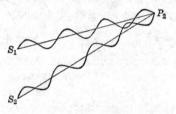

Figure 34

one-half wavelengths from source S_1 and four wave-lengths from source S_2. Always, when a crest reaches P_2 from S_1, a trough reaches P_2 from S_2; there is never any wave at P_2, for the waves from the two sources always cancel at this point and, indeed, everywhere in this direction from the two sources.

The Focusing of Waves and Its Limitations

By means of the principles we have just discussed, we can explain how it is that *microwaves*—that is, radio waves a few centimeters or less in length—as well as the rays of light, can be focused by a lens. A material such as glass will transmit electromagnetic waves, but in it the waves go slower than they do in air. Thus, the wavelength, which is the velocity divided by the frequency, is shorter in the glass of a lens than it is in the air about the lens. Fig. 35 illustrates a lens focusing electromagnetic waves from point *a* onto point *b*.

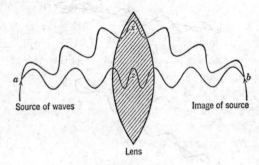

Figure 35

We know that to the left of the lens the waves travel out in straight lines from the source *a*, as shown. We can see how they must travel to a focus to the right of the lens if at the focus crest is to be added to crest and trough to trough. They must travel as shown, in such a way that the indirect path *a–x–b*, which is longer than the direct path *a–z–b*, contains just the same number of wavelengths as the direct path. The shorter path *a–z–b* passes through a greater thickness of glass, and the wavelength is shorter in the glass than in the air, just as shown. Thus it is that the shorter and longer paths contain the same number of wavelengths. The lens will focus all the waves from *a* at *b* because it is so shaped that all the paths similar to path *a–x–b* which pass through it contain the same number of wavelengths; at *b* crest will be added to crest and trough to trough for all paths.

This explanation of how lenses focus light may

come as something of a shock even to people who think they know a little about optics. One aspect of optics is called *geometrical optics*. In geometrical optics we grandly draw in lines representing *rays* of light, and we show how rays are bent when they pass from air into glass. All this was worked out before the physical nature of light, that is, its wave nature, was understood. Even now that we know the nature of light we still use geometrical optics for many purposes. It is a good approximation to the behavior of the waves when, and only when, the waves are very short compared with the size of the lenses and of the images we are considering.

To find the full truth about the behavior of lenses and other optical devices, however, we must turn to *physical optics*, to explanations based on waves. This is what we have just done in explaining how a lens focuses waves. This description is important not only because it explains how a lens focuses light but also because it explains certain limitations on focusing which are vitally important in microwave radio and in optics.

To understand the limitations of focusing, let us begin with a question. What do we mean when we say, regarding Fig. 35, that the waves are *focused* at *b*? If we move a little up or down from *b*, the waves from *a* will still add up, crest with crest and trough with trough. It is clear that the waves cannot be focused precisely on one point, but rather that they will spread out over an area. Just as waves don't make perfectly sharp shadows, they don't make perfectly sharp images.

In fact, we can easily estimate how sharp the image can be. Fig. 36 shows a lens of width D focusing waves on a point b a distance L from the lens. The lens has been divided into two halves; the centers of each half, at x and y, are a distance $D/2$ apart. Suppose that we move up a distance W from b to a point b'. The distance W is such that the distance from b' to the center of the lower half of the lens is just half a wavelength, $\lambda/2$, greater than the distance from b' to the center of the upper half of the lens. Roughly speaking, at this point b', crests of the waves from the lower half of the lens will arrive when troughs of the waves from the upper part of the lens arrive. That is, there will be no waves at b'.

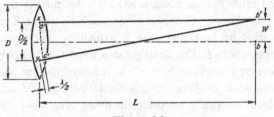

Figure 36

Let us consider the long, narrow equilateral triangle $a'b'c'$, shown in Fig. 36. Its length or altitude is very nearly L. The width of its base is very nearly $D/2$. We can regard the triangle as a sort of lever. The condition we have described in which the waves cancel at b', requires that c' be a distance $\lambda/2$ from the point y. When we move c' a small distance $\lambda/2$ from y, keeping a' at x, b' will move some distance W above b. If the triangle is long and narrow the ratio of W to $\lambda/2$ will be, almost exactly, the ratio of the lever arms L and $D/2$, so that

$$\frac{W}{(\lambda/2)} = \frac{L}{(D/2)}$$

or

$$\frac{W}{L} = \frac{\lambda}{D}$$

Thus, waves will fall above and below b, but at approximately W above and below b there will be no waves at all. As a matter of fact, a great fraction of the waves will fall in a range from $W/2$ above b to $W/2$ below b.

This is an extremely important fact, both in radio and in optics. It can be shown to apply when waves are focused by concave mirrors as well as when waves are focused by lenses. It says, for instance, that if we have a radar antenna of width D and send out a beam of microwaves of wavelength λ to a distance L, the beam will have a width W given by this relation. For instance, for radar waves 10 centimeters, or $\frac{1}{3}$ foot, long and an antenna 10 feet wide, at a distance of one mile, or 5280 feet, the width W of the radar beam will be about

$$W = \frac{\frac{1}{3}(5280)}{10}$$
$$W = 176 \text{ feet}$$

For waves 1 centimeter long instead of 10 centimeters long, the beam would be only 17.6 feet wide. This tenfold difference in beam width at the target shows why it is important to use short waves and large antennas in order to locate airplanes accurately by radar.

By similar arguments it can be shown that if we have a telescope lens or mirror of width D, and if we use light of wavelength λ, and if we look at two points or patches of light a distance L away, we can *resolve* them—that is, see them as two separate patches or points of light—only if they are at least a distance W apart, where W is given by this same relation.

For instance, light waves are about 2×10^{-6} feet long. The distance to Mars at its nearest is about 3.5×10^7 miles, or about 1.8×10^{11} feet. If we have a telescope with a lens or mirror 1 foot in diameter, we can resolve objects if they are a distance W apart, given by

$$W = \frac{(2 \times 10^{-6})(1.8 \times 10^{11})}{1}$$
$$W = 360,000 \text{ feet}$$
$$W = 70 \text{ miles}$$

Telescopes and Microscopes

Giovanni Schiaparelli, who in 1877 first reported seeing canals on Mars and who asserted later that they were sometimes double, used a telescope with a lens a little less than $\frac{3}{4}$ foot in diameter. Thus, he could not have seen double canals unless they were at least 100 miles apart, and he could scarcely have detected single canals unless they were around 100 miles wide. Even the 200-inch telescope could not possibly resolve details on Mars of a size smaller than about 4 miles. On the moon, however, it could resolve details down to about 160 feet.

The same limits to resolution which apply in telescopes apply in microscopes also. This explains why we can see so much finer detail with an electron microscope than with a light microscope. Biologists had to wait for the advent of the electron microscope to be able to see viruses, and the electron microscope has revealed hitherto hidden details of the structure of metals to metallurgists.

Quantum mechanics tells us that when we examine the behavior of electrons in very fine detail, we see phenomena of a wave nature. In fact, the simple behavior of electrons as particles, which we discussed in the preceding chapter, bears much the same relation to the fine-grained quantum-mechanical behavior of electrons that geometric optics does to wave optics. We must consider the wave nature of electrons when we ask how good the resolving power of an electron microscope can be.

The wavelength of an electron varies inversely as the square root of the voltage used to accelerate the electrons. For a 50,000-volt accelerating voltage, which is common in electron microscopy, the electron wavelength is about 2×10^{-10} inch. This is roughly a hundred-thousandth the wavelength of visible light.

Using optical microscopes with visible light, we cannot possibly achieve resolutions of better than about a hundred-thousandth of an inch (10^{-5} inches). If we could judge by wavelength alone, an electron microscope would be a hundred thousand times as good as a light microscope. But because electron lenses are much inferior in quality to lenses for light, an electron microscope has a resolving power only about a thousand times better than a light microscope. Thus, with an electron microscope we can resolve objects down to about a hundred-millionth of an inch (10^{-8} inch).

Microwave Transmission

Resolution is important in telescopes and microscopes. The width of a radio beam is important in microwave communication. Microwave transmitters send out beams of microwaves from horns, lenses, or reflectors which are called *antennas*. Fig. 37 illustrates some common types of antennas used in transmitting and receiving microwaves. Microwaves are often guided for short distances through metal tubes or *wave guides*. In the antenna shown to the left in Fig. 37, the wave guide flares out to form a horn like a megaphone, and a lens is placed at the end of the horn. In the antenna shown at the center, the waves from the end of the wave guide are focused into a beam by a concave metal dish in the form of a *parabola*. Most radar antennas are of this sort. In the *horn-reflector* antenna shown at the right of Fig. 37

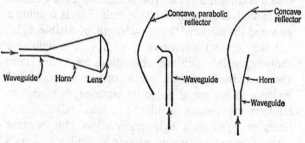

Figure 37

the waves from the horn are focused by a concave surface set at an angle.

Large antennas are necessarily highly directive.

Large, highly directive antennas are used in micro-wave communication systems so that the transmitted power can be sent toward the receiver rather than scattered in all directions, and so that the receiver can pick up power over a large area. We can see just how this works out. Fig. 38 shows a microwave transmitter and a microwave receiver. The transmitter sends out a beam of microwaves. A receiving antenna a distance L away picks up a part of this beam. According to our relation, if D is the diameter of the transmitting

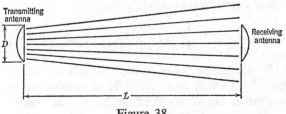

Figure 38

antenna and λ is the wavelength, the width, W, of the microwave beam at the receiving antenna is about

$$W = \frac{\lambda L}{D}$$

If we assume the beam to be circular, the area, A, over which it falls is approximately the area of a circle of diameter W, that is,

$$A = \frac{\pi}{4}W^2 = \frac{\pi\lambda^2 L^2}{4D^2}$$

If A_R is the area of the receiving antenna, the ratio of the power, P_R, which falls on the receiving antenna and is received to the total power transmitted in the beam, which we will call P_T, is

$$\frac{P_R}{P_T} = \frac{A_R}{A} = \frac{4A_R D^2}{\pi \lambda^2 L^2}$$

If the transmitting antenna is circular, its area, A_T, is

$$A_T = \frac{\pi}{4} D^2$$

or

$$D^2 = \frac{4}{\pi} A_T$$

Thus, we can write approximately for the ratio of received power to transmitted power,

$$\frac{P_R}{P_T} = \left(\frac{4}{\pi}\right)^2 \frac{A_R A_T}{\lambda^2 L^2}$$

This relation has been arrived at right before our eyes. We have derived everything in it, including the expression for the width of the beam. The result is only approximate because we have used an approximate expression for the diameter of the area over which the transmitted power falls. The correct expression is

$$\frac{P_R}{P_T} = \frac{A_R A_T}{\lambda^2 L^2}$$

This simple and basic equation governing microwave transmission was derived by H. T. Friis. It tells us that to increase the fraction of the transmitted power received at a distance L from the transmitter we should increase the area of the transmitting antenna, or the area of the receiving antenna, or we should use a shorter wavelength. In this expression, A_R and A_T are the actual physical areas of the transmitting and receiving antennas only for ideal antennas.

An ideal transmitting antenna sends out a wave of equal strength over its whole area. If an antenna is ideal as a transmitting antenna, it is ideal as a receiving antenna. Actual practical antennas are not ideal, and we must use instead of A_T and A_R the *effective areas*, which are less than the actual geometrical areas but usually somewhat greater than one half of the geometrical areas. The effective area of antenna is the same for transmitting as for receiving.

For a typical microwave radio circuit, the distance L is around 30 miles, or 150,000 feet. The antennas may be square and 10 feet on a side. The effective area may be one half the geometrical area, so that A_T and A_R are each 50 square feet. λ may be around 7.5 centimeters—that is, 3 inches, or $\frac{1}{4}$ feet. Thus,

$$\frac{P_R}{P_T} = \frac{(50)\,(50)}{(\frac{1}{4})^2(150,000)^2} = 1.8 \times 10^{-6}$$

Only about two millionths of the transmitted power will be received.

So far we have considered the properties of waves traveling through open spaces: waves sent out and picked up by antennas and waves focused by lenses and mirrors. There is another very important kind of wave called a *standing wave*. It is a wave that has been trapped in one place. Let us consider how a wave can be trapped.

Reflection and the Standing Wave

First we must understand how a wave is reflected. Fig. 39 represents the reflection, by a reflecting surface R, of a wave coming from the left. The wave from the left is shown as a solid curve; the reflected wave is shown as a dotted curve.

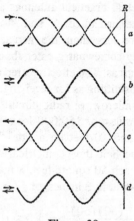

Figure 39

Reflections are of various kinds. Sometimes the reflection leaves the wave right side up, reflecting a crest as a crest and a trough as a trough. Sometimes (I will present evidence for this later) a reflection turns the wave upside down, reflecting a crest as a trough and a trough as a crest. The reflection in Fig. 39 is of this latter kind. In sketch *b* the wave traveling from the left has advanced a quarter wavelength from where it was in sketch *a*, and so has the reflected wave. Sketch *c* shows another advance of a quarter wavelength. Sketch *d* shows an advance of a quarter wavelength more.

We remember that waves are a linear phenomenon, and to get the total amplitude of the waves in Fig. 39 we add the amplitudes of the two waves. When both are equal and positive at the same point, or equal and negative at the same point, as in *b* and *d*, the total amplitude is twice the amplitude of either wave. When one wave is as positive as the other is negative, as in *a* and *c*, the total amplitude is zero. In Fig. 40 the amplitudes of the incident and reflected waves have been added according to this rule. We see that the wave pattern moves neither to the right nor to the

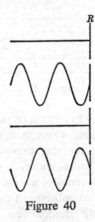

Figure 40

left. We have a *standing*, not a *traveling* wave. At the reflector, and at half a wavelength, two half wavelengths and three halves of a wavelength to the left of it, the total amplitude is always zero. At other points, the amplitude rises and falls periodically with time, with the frequency, f, of the wave.

Suppose we put two reflectors, R_1 and R_2, half a wavelength apart, as shown in Fig. 41. The solid curve shows the maximum upper excursion of the standing wave; the dashed curve shows the maximum lower excursion of the standing wave. The wave successively oscillates through all positions in between.

If Fig. 41 strikingly resembles the vibration of a stretched rubber band, a door spring, or the string of a musical instrument, the resemblance is intentional. All are examples of standing waves, of waves which are reflected back and forth endlessly. If there were no

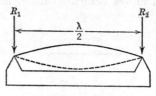

Figure 41

dissipation of energy in friction or radiation of energy in the form of traveling waves, such waves would persist forever. In our ordinary experience such waves eventually die out, unless energy is supplied. The vibration of the struck string of a piano dies out because no energy is supplied subsequent to the blow of the hammer, while both friction and the radiation of sound carry energy away. The standing wave in the organ pipe persists because the blower continues to supply energy.

Unless the wavelength is exactly $\lambda/2$ or $2\lambda/2$ or $3\lambda/2$, as in Fig. 42, the wave will not be properly reflected at each end to maintain the pattern, and the pattern cannot exist. As the wavelength and the frequency are related, a standing wave between reflectors a fixed distance apart can exist only at certain particular frequencies and in certain particular patterns. If the velocity is independent of frequency, and if we

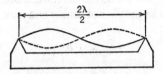

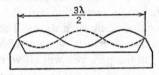

Figure 42

say that the pattern of Fig. 42 corresponds to some fundamental frequency f_1, the pattern of the upper part of Fig. 42 will have a frequency $f_2 = 2f_1$, the *second harmonic* (also, the *first overtone*, which is an octave up). The pattern of the lower part of Fig. 42 will have a frequency $f_3 = 3f_1$, the *third harmonic* (the second overtone, the fifth above the octave above). Many such patterns can exist simultaneously without interfering with one another because the oscillating string is a linear system, just as waves caused by dropping pebbles in a pond can pass through one another without disturbing one another. In striking a piano string we produce many overtones, and these and the way in which they decay with time are responsible for the characteristic tone quality of the piano.

Sometimes, as in the case of stretched strings, the overtones have frequencies that are integral multiples of the fundamental frequency (an integer is 1, 2, 3, 4, etc.). This is true for stretched strings. Sometimes it is otherwise, as in the case of drums and bells.

Trapped Waves

Let us disregard the oversimplified illustrations we have used and talk about all trapped waves—waves which cannot escape because, no matter in which way they travel, they meet a reflecting barrier.

We can think of many such waves. The ripples on the surface of the water in a pan are reflected by the walls. If you tap the pan, you will (if you are lucky) see concentric rings on the surface; these are standing waves. Electromagnetic (radio) waves can be trapped in a metal box, for metal reflects radio waves.

Any closed (to the waves) system that can support waves traps them. The system may be a violin string, a tuning fork, a room, or a metal box. Such a system will support waves of certain frequencies only. Such frequencies, and the wave patterns associated with them, have been known for many years. They used to be called *normal modes*. *Modes* means merely patterns of oscillation. Since the advent of quantum mechanics, which came mainly from Germany, the patterns have been called *eigenfunctions* and the frequencies *eigenfrequencies*. On a small enough scale electrons behave as waves, and in quantum physics the atom is an oscillator exhibiting certain patterns of standing waves.

We are not primarily interested in atoms; our interest is in radio and electronics. We should spend some time on electromagnetic waves trapped in metallic enclosures, for they are very important.

Let us make a rather symbolic drawing, shown in

Fig. 43. R_1 and R_2 represent somewhat imperfect reflectors. Between R_1 and R_2 there can exist a standing wave. Reflectors R_1 and R_2 have little holes in them, however, and allow some of the waves to leak out at each reflection. Thus, if nothing were done, the standing wave between R_1 and R_2 would die out

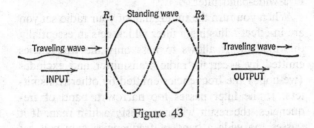

Figure 43

as time passed. For instance, a weak wave would leak off to the right of R_2. An arrow shows its direction of travel, and the arrow is labeled *output*.

If we had only the wave leaking off, the standing wave pattern between R_1 and R_2 would gradually decrease in amplitude. Suppose, however, that we supply a wave from the left, which is shown together with an arrow indicating its direction of travel. The arrow is labeled *input*.

If the holes in the reflectors R_1 and R_2 are very small, we can hope to get a wave through this system only if the frequency is exactly the value that makes the distance between R_1 and R_2 a wavelength, so that the large standing wave which is indicated can exist. Imagine the opposite extreme; suppose we make the holes so large that the reflectors cease to exist. We have an uninterrupted medium for transmission of waves between input and output, and waves of any frequency can get through.

What we have just described is a *filter* for electromagnetic waves. Such a filter passes waves of a certain range of frequencies only, a narrow range or *band* of frequencies, or a wide range or band of frequencies, depending on its adjustment. In our example, small holes result in a narrow-band filter and large holes in a wide-band filter.

When you turn the tuning dial of your radio set you are in effect adjusting a filter which acts in essentially this manner. It allows to pass only the frequencies emitted by a certain radio transmitter and excludes (we hope) the frequencies emitted by other transmitters. If the filter passes too narrow a band of frequencies, the result will not satisfy a hi-fi man. If it passes too wide a band of frequencies, you will get two or more stations at once.

What then have we learned in this chapter about waves? Not much in minute detail. Saying that we have five horses tells us little about horses. Saying that we have five wives raises questions which cannot be resolved by mathematics.

The Concept of Waves

Number is a very general concept, but one of overwhelming scope and importance. The idea of waves is a somewhat more complicated concept, and one of a smaller range of applicability. Yet, after the ideas of number and measurement, it is among the few concepts of very great generality. Without the concept of waves, we cannot understand the behavior of the ocean, of earthquakes, of sound of musical instruments, of the vibration of structures, of radio, of light, nor, we must emphasize, of that bane of those who are imperfectly adjusted to contemporary physics; that is, quantum mechanics.

In studying waves further, we must pay some heed to the physical nature of the waves which we study. Ordinarily, a student of physics starts out with mechanical waves of some sort.

In mechanical waves, the propagation of waves always involves kinetic energy and potential energy, the two forms of energy discussed toward the end of Chapter Two. The material through which the wave propagates moves with an oscillatory motion. Because of the velocity associated with this motion, the material gains and loses kinetic energy. In sound waves the air is compressed as the wave travels; the air under pressure has potential energy. In large waves of water, the water has potential energy because at the crests it is raised above the mean level. In small ripples, the water has potential energy because of the stretching of the surface of the water against *surface tension*. As the wave travels along, the material through which it travels alternately gains and loses kinetic and potential energy.

Newton's laws of motion tell us that in altering the velocity which accounts for kinetic energy, a force must be exerted; this force is the force associated with the increase or decrease of potential energy as the material is distorted during the passage of the wave.

If this were a conventional treatment of waves, we would analyze in detail the propagation of one or more types of mechanical waves, to show how the laws of motion explain their behavior and how the waves transmit energy away from the device that produces them and carry it to whatever absorbs them. This book is, however, primarily an account of electronics, and in explaining in detail the behavior of waves we will consider only the case of electromagnetic waves. For an understanding of electromagnetic waves, we must understand Maxwell's equations, which govern the behavior of electric and magnetic fields. Maxwell's equations form the subject of the following chapter.

Chapter Six

MAXWELL'S WONDERFUL EQUATIONS

There are certain summits of achievement in the history of science, the formulation of certain general laws, which command the profound respect of all following generations. Newton's laws of motion together with his law of gravitation are one such an eminence. Newton's work makes it possible to unravel all the phenomena associated with mechanical motions. After Newton's day, a knowledge of physics which did not include an understanding of Newton's work was inconceivable.

Maxwell's equations are for electric and magnetic phenomena what Newton's laws are for mechanical phenomena. While later advances such as relativity and quantum mechanics have followed, an understanding of this newer knowledge of the universe presupposes an understanding of Newton's laws and of Maxwell's equations. Maxwell's equations are fundamental not only to electronics but to all physics. To anyone who is motivated by anything beyond the most narrowly practical, it is worth while to understand Maxwell's equations simply for the good of the soul.

Those who work in electronics have to understand Maxwell's equations to some degree, for these equations govern the behavior of electric and magnetic fields. Sometimes the understanding appears in a rather specialized form, as in certain particular rules which govern the behavior of coils and capacitors in radio circuits. All these particular rules stem from Maxwell's equations.

It was with some trepidation that I tackled the problem of explaining Maxwell's equations in this book. I have several thick reference books which deal with nothing but Maxwell's equations and examples of their application in various practical problems. Each book is longer than this book, and all are much tougher reading.

Usually the student is brought to some understanding of Maxwell's equations by easy stages, through dealing first with certain simple and specialized behavior of electric and magnetic fields, including the way charges produce electric fields and the way currents produce magnetic fields. Then Maxwell's equations are presented as a synthesis of this behavior. There follows a mathematical study of the equations, by means of which certain general forms of behavior of fields are deduced as mathematical theorems. Maxwell's equations are then used to solve particular problems involving electric and magnetic fields.

There is just not space here for that sort of thing, nor can the reader be presumed to have the time or the mathematics to wade through it.

Oliver Heaviside was an important and eccentric physicist and electrical engineer of the latter part of the last century and the early part of this. In his book on electricity and magnetism, he simply stated Maxwell's equations. He then applied them to explain the behavior of a particularly simple phenomenon, a plane electromagnetic wave. He turned to more complicated problems later. We will follow a similar course, except that we cannot apply the equations to as many problems as Heaviside did in writing for experts in his field.

Fortunately for this approach, we already have the necessary notions of electric and magnetic fields and of their representation by lines of force. We should remember that the lines of force show the direction of the field and that the density or closeness of the lines of force indicates the strength of the field. Because a field is a vector, which has a magnitude and a direction (the direction of the lines of force), we can resolve the field into components, and we can speak of the component of the field in any direction we choose. Thus, in Fig. 44 the line with the two arrowheads is a chosen direction and the vector

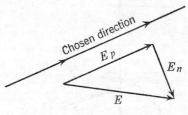

Figure 44

E is the electric field. To find the component E_p parallel to the chosen direction we draw two vectors, E_p parallel to the direction and E_n normal to the direction, such that the vector sum of E_p and E_n is equal to E. Then E_p is the component of field in the chosen direction and E_n is the component normal to that direction.

Electric and Magnetic Fluxes

In order to understand Maxwell's equations in the simplest possible terms, it is helpful to become familiar with two important quantities called *electric flux* and *magnetic flux*. The electric and magnetic fluxes are quantities that can be expressed in terms of the electric and magnetic fields. They are useful quantities. They enter into Maxwell's equations in a particular way which we shall see. We should not, however, look for some mysterious meaning of these quantities. They are just what we define them to be. We should ask, then, how are these fluxes defined?

Imagine, as in Fig. 45, that we have an electric field of strength E perpendicular to a small flat area

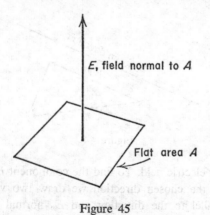

E, field normal to A

Flat area A

Figure 45

A. Then the electric flux, which I will call ϕ (phi), is a constant ϵ times the field strength, E, times the area, A.

$$\phi = \epsilon E A$$

ϵ (epsilon) is called the dielectric constant of space. Similarly, for a magnetic field of strength H normal to the area A, the magnetic flux ψ (psi) is given by

$$\psi = \mu H A$$

where μ (mu) is called the permeability of space.

Because the strength of a field is proportional to the density of lines of force, the flux through an area is proportional to the number of lines of force crossing that area.

Suppose we want to calculate the flux across an area which is not normal to the electric or magnetic field. To do this, we draw a line normal to the area, as in Fig. 46, and multiply the area by the component of field which is parallel to this line. We call this

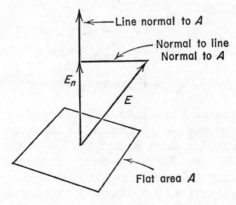

Figure 46

normal component E_n or H_n. Thus, we should really write for electric flux ϕ and magnetic flux ψ

$$\phi = \epsilon E_n A$$
$$\psi = \mu H_n A$$

You should notice that when we draw a line normal to the area A, we have to draw it in some direction. In Fig. 46 the line could have pointed either up or down, but in the figure it points up, as indicated by the arrowhead on its end. If the normal component of the field, E_n or H_n, lies in the same direction as the line, the flux will be positive; if it lies in the opposite direction, then the normal component of the field and the flux corresponding to it will be negative.

Another thing important in understanding Maxwell's equations is the idea of a field component along a curve. Fig. 47 shows a closed curve l, and we con-

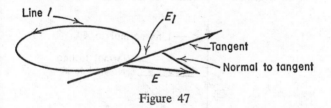

Figure 47

sider this curve to have some direction indicated by the arrowhead. At any point on l we can draw a line tangent to l, as shown in the figure. The tangent will have the same direction as the curve. Now, where the tangent touches the curve there will be some electric field E. If we draw a line from the arrow-end of the vector E normal to the tangent, we obtain the field component along the curve l at the point in question. This component E_l lies along the tangent, and its length or magnitude is the distance between the point of tangency and the place where the normal from the head of the field vector E meets the tangent. We can see that E_l can be positive if E_l points in the direction of l and its tangent, or negative if E_l points in the direction opposite to that of l and its tangent.

Suppose that we have a cap-shaped surface as shown in Fig. 48. The particular shape of the surface doesn't matter; what will be said is true of any surface, and I have chosen this shape merely because it is easy to draw. I have divided this surface into

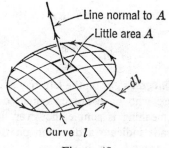

Figure 48

little areas, so small that we can consider them to be flat. One of these I have labeled A. I have drawn a line normal or perpendicular to this area A, and I have indicated a direction on it by means of arrowheads. We get the flux through this little area A by taking the component of field parallel to this line and in the direction indicated and by multiplying the field by the area. This flux may thus be positive or negative, depending on whether the component of field is in the direction of the arrowheads or in the opposite direction. We can get the total flux through the whole

surface bounded by the curve *l*, which runs around
the perimeter of the surface in the direction indicated
by the arrowheads, by adding together the fluxes for
all the little areas into which the surface has been
divided.

Flux and Displacement Current

Once we have clearly in our mind what electric
and magnetic flux are—that is, what we have defined
them to be—it is easy to understand Maxwell's equations. We can write them in the following form:

$$\oint H_l dl = \frac{\partial \phi}{\partial t} + I_o$$

$$\oint E_l dl = - \frac{\partial \psi}{\partial t}$$

The *line integral signs* on the left may appear caba-
listic to those who have not encountered them before. Their meaning is simple, however. In Fig. 48
the arrowheads indicate a direction on the curve *l*
which runs around the boundary of the surface.
Moreover, a little length *dl* of the boundary has been
indicated. Suppose that we take the component of
magnetic field H_l parallel to this little line *dl* and in
the direction of the arrowheads. Let us multiply this
component H_l by the length *dl*, and then do this for
all other little lengths, once around the perimeter,
and finally add up all the products. This sum is what
we mean by the *line integral*

$$\oint H_l dl$$

What do we mean by $\partial \phi / \partial t$? This means the rate
at which the electric flux changes with time. $\partial \psi / \partial t$ is

the rate at which magnetic flux changes with time. These symbols mean the amount the flux changes in an extremely short period of time divided by the length of that period of time, measured in seconds.

I_c stands for the total current carried by charged particles which flow across the total area bounded by l, the flow in the direction of the arrowheads on the line normal to the surface. Of course, this current may be positive or negative, depending on which way the current flows with respect to the arrowheads on the line.

We notice that in the first of Maxwell's equations the quantity $\partial\phi/\partial t$ is added to the current I_c. As we noted in Chapter Four, an electric current—that is, a flow of electric charges—produces a magnetic field. Maxwell was the first to recognize that a change in electric flux acts just as does a flow of charges in producing a magnetic field. Because $\partial\phi/\partial t$ behaves like a flow of charges, $\partial\phi/\partial t$ is reckoned as part of the total electric current. It is called *displacement current* (there are historical reasons for the word *displacement* which need not concern us). To distinguish the part of the current I_c which is due to the flow of charges I_c is called *convection current*. We may add these two parts of the current together to get the total current, I:

$$I = \frac{\partial\phi}{\partial t} + I_c$$

Although the quantity $\partial\psi/\partial t$, which appears in the second of Maxwell's equations, has no name, we may if we wish call it *magnetic displacement current*. Because there are no free magnetic poles, there is no such thing as magnetic convection current.

We are now in a position to state Maxwell's equations in words. The first equation says that if, with due regard for sign and direction, we go once around the boundary of a region, multiply each element of the length of the boundary by the component of magnetic field in the direction of the boundary, and add all these products up, then the total is equal to the total current, convection current and displacement current, flowing through the boundary. Or, mathematically, the line integral of the magnetic field around the boundary is equal to the total current through the boundary. This equation has to do with the production of magnetic fields by the flow of charges and by displacement current—that is, by changes in electric fields.

Maxwell's second equation says that the line integral of the electric field around the boundary is equal to the negative of the rate of change of magnetic flux through the boundary; that is, to the negative of the magnetic displacement current through the boundary. This equation has to do with the production of electric fields by changes in magnetic fields.

In interpreting this second equation, we should remember that the work done on a moving charge is the magnitude of the charge times the component of electric field in the direction of motion, times the distance moved. Thus, if we moved an electric charge around the line l of Fig. 48 fast enough so that the field did not change appreciably while we moved the charge, the work done on the charge would be just the charge times the line integral of the electric field—that is, times the left-hand side of Maxwell's second equation. Magnetic fields cannot do work on electric charges, but a changing magnetic flux will produce electric fields which can do work on moving electric charges.

The Betatron

Indeed, this is the principle of the betatron. The betatron is an electron accelerator. It is used to produce very fast electrons. The first betatrons were used in experiments in nuclear physics. Nowadays the fast electrons from betatrons are often used to produce very penetrating X rays which can be used to make X-ray photographs of heavy steel parts, and which have been used in treating cancer.

Electron velocity, and hence the kinetic energy of electrons, is often specified in *electron volts* or simply *volts*. This means the voltage which would be necessary to accelerate an electron to a particular velocity and kinetic energy. Betatrons give electrons energies of tens of millions of electron volts. Betatrons are huge, heavy beasts, consisting principally of an electromagnet whose iron core and copper coils weigh many tons. A glass, doughnut-shaped, evacuated tube is placed between the poles of the magnet, and the electrons which are to be accelerated travel around and around in circles inside the doughnut. The magnet is so designed that the magnetic flux through the circle of the electron path is twice what it would be if the magnetic field had the same strength over all of the area of the circle that it has at the electron path itself.

The magnetic field serves two purposes. It bends the electrons in their paths so that they can circle around inside the doughnut. Then, as the electrons circle around, the magnetic field is made to increase in strength. According to Maxwell's second equation, this produces an electric field along the circular electron path, in such a direction as to increase the speed of the electrons. It is this field that accelerates the electrons in their paths until they have tens of millions of volts energy. If the magnetic flux through the circular path is adjusted as stated above, the diameter of the circular electron path will remain constant as the electrons are accelerated.

The example of the betatron shows one application of Maxwell's second equation. Another is the case in which a wire or a coil of wire which is part of an electric circuit moves physically through a magnetic field so that the magnetic flux through the complete circuit changes. In one type of microphone for picking up sound waves, a moving diaphragm moves a coil of wire in a magnetic field so as to produce an electric field which is a representation of the sound wave. Electric generators also work in this manner. Many other things, simple and complicated, can be understood if once we become familiar with Maxwell's equations and learn to remember the meaning of the quantities that appear in them. In fact, they tell what there is to be known about the behavior of electric and magnetic fields.

The Plane Electromagnetic Wave

They tell their full story, however, only to those who are able to extract information from them by means of mathematical transformations and manipulations. Here we must content ourselves with a few simple examples. I trust, however, that even some of these may prove a little startling as well as important and interesting.

It is very hard even for the mathematically expert to find combinations of changing electric and magnetic fields which are solutions of Maxwell's equations. We can, however, test any proposed electric and magnetic fields. If they do not satisfy Maxwell's equations the proposed fields cannot represent real physical phenomena. Conversely, if in some way we find electric and magnetic fields which do satisfy Maxwell's equations, these fields do represent possible physical phenomena, things which could take place and be observed in the world about us. Let us now consider one simple, possible combination of electric and magnetic fields—that which Oliver Heaviside placed at the beginning of his book, the plane electromagnetic wave.

By *plane* wave we mean one which does not expand in circles as it travels, as do the ripples from a stone in a pond, but one which travels everywhere in one direction. Strictly speaking, one cannot produce plane electromagnetic waves of the sort we shall discuss. However, suppose that an electromagnetic wave travels out radially from a source such as a radio antenna. Very far from the antenna, a wave crest will be spherical in form. When the sphere is large enough, the wave is nearly plane, and just as the surface of the earth can be regarded as plane for many purposes, we can in our considerations regard such a wave crest as lying in a plane.

Fig. 49 is intended to illustrate a portion of a plane wave. The rightmost part of the wave is called the *wave front*; this lies in a plane normal to the direc-

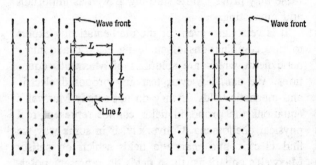

Figure 49

tion of propagation and, in the figure, normal to the plane of the paper. To the left of the wave front there is a uniform magnetic field of strength H, directed upward, and a uniform electric field of strength E points straight into the plane of the paper, away from us. To the right of the wave front there is no electric or magnetic field. The wave travels through air or vacuum, where there are no electric charges, so there is no convection current. The wave front travels to the right with a velocity v.

As our line l we will take a square of length L on a side, with its surface parallel to the magnetic field and perpendicular to the electric field. We will consider conditions at two succeeding times; just after the wave front has barely passed the left-hand side of the square, and just before it reaches the right-hand side of the square.

In each case, there is no component of magnetic field along the top or the bottom of the square, and the field has not yet reached the right-hand side of the square. Thus, there is a component of magnetic field along the left-hand side of the square only, and the line integral around the square is simply

$$\oint H_l dl = HL$$

The wave takes a time T to cross the square of width L, where T is given by

$$T = \frac{L}{v}$$

At the start of this time, the electric flux through the square is zero; at the end of the time T it is

$$\phi = \epsilon E L^2$$

The rate of change of the flux is this total change of flux divided by the time, T, or

$$\frac{\partial \phi}{\partial t} = \frac{\phi}{T} = \epsilon E L \frac{L}{T} = \epsilon E L v$$

According to Maxwell's first equation,

$$HL = \frac{\partial \phi}{\partial t} = \epsilon E L v$$

$$H = \epsilon E v$$

Suppose that we now consider a square parallel to the electric field and perpendicular to the magnetic field. We find that:

$$\oint E_l dl = EL$$

$$\psi = -\mu H L^2$$

$$\frac{\partial \psi}{\partial t} = \frac{\psi}{T} = -\mu H L \frac{L}{T} = -\mu H L v$$

The sign is negative because of the direction of the field with respect to the directions indicated in Fig. 49.

According to Maxwell's second equation,

$$EL = -\frac{\partial \psi}{\partial t} = \mu H L v$$

$$E = \mu H v$$

We now have both this and the earlier relation between E and H to work with, that is,

$$H = \epsilon E v$$

If we multiply the two relations between E and H together, we obtain

$$EH = \mu \epsilon E H v^2$$

This gives

$$v^2 = \frac{1}{\mu \epsilon}$$

$$v = \frac{1}{\sqrt{\mu \epsilon}}$$

If we put in the numerical values of μ and ϵ in the appendix we find that $v = 3 \times 10^8$ meters per second. This is just the velocity of light. When Maxwell first deduced electromagnetic waves from his equations, it was this fact that led him to believe, correctly, that light is simply electromagnetic waves.

We can divide the two relations for E and H and obtain

$$\frac{H}{E} = \frac{\epsilon E}{\mu H}$$

$$\frac{E}{H} = \sqrt{\frac{\mu}{\epsilon}} = 377$$

This is a relation that is very important to those who work with electromagnetic waves. It holds true for all plane electromagnetic waves, whether they vary with distance in the direction of motion in the abrupt manner of the wave which we have just considered or vary sinusoidally with time and distance.

When waves vary sinusoidally with time, the electric and magnetic fields are perpendicular to one another and normal to the direction of travel, just as in the wave described above. As the wave moves past a point, the electric field and the magnetic field at the point rise and fall in intensity. The magnetic field is at its peak at the same time that the electric field is at its peak.

Imagine that we turn the drawing of Fig. 49 around so that the bottom becomes the top. The electric field still points away from us. The magnetic field, which formerly pointed up, now points down. And the wave now travels to the left instead of to the right.

Radiation from a Current

I have tried to illustrate this in Fig. 50. To the right of the heavy vertical line A–A', the electric field E is away from us, the magnetic field H is upward, and the wave travels to the right. To the left of line A–A', the electric field is away from us, the magnetic field is downward, and the wave travels to the left.

Can we have a situation of this kind? I have shown a rectangle of height h and very narrow width which just encloses the dividing line A–A'. We see that the line integral of H around this path is

$$\oint H dl = -2Hh$$

According to Maxwell's first equation, this must be equal to the sum of the displacement current plus the convection current through the rectangle. If we make the rectangle very, very narrow, the electric flux through it must be negligibly small. Thus we must have

$$-2Hh = I_c$$

This equation means that the condition we have imagined can exist if along the line $A-A'$ a convection current, a current of moving charges, flows through the rectangle, normal to the plane of the paper. The current per unit distance along the line $A-A'$ must be such that $2H$ amperes flow for each meter of distance along $A-A'$. The positive direction

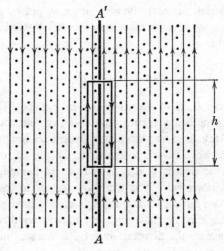

Figure 50

has been taken as the direction into the plane of the paper, the direction of the electric field. As the above relation says that the current must be negative, the direction of current flow will be opposite to the direction of the electric field—that is, out of the plane of the paper. If the current consisted of negative electrons, the electrons would flow into the plane of the paper, in the same direction as the electric field.

The electric force on a charged particle is the charge times the field. As the charge of the electron is negative, the force on the electrons constituting the current will be up from the plane of the paper, against their motion. Thus, to make them move in the direction necessary to produce the electromagnetic waves which go off to the left and right, we must push the electrons constituting the current in the direction of motion; we must do work on them. To cause the current to flow, work must be done; and power, the rate at which this work is done, must be supplied. This power flows away to the left and to the right in the form of the electromagnetic power of the waves, which the flowing current generates.

In order to make the arguments as simple as possible, the electromagnetic waves discussed in connection with Figs. 49 and 50 are waves in which the electric and magnetic fields do not vary with time or distance (except abruptly at the wave front in the wave of Fig. 49). The electromagnetic waves actually used in radio vary sinusoidally with time and distance. And, if we wish, we can imagine Fig. 50 to apply to a sinusoidal current, which flows first in one direction and then in the other, so that the fields the current sends out to the left and right rise and fall in amplitude, and are in opposite directions during succeeding halves of the cycle of variation.

It may be helpful to consider a perspective drawing representing the electric and magnetic fields of a plain sinusoidal electromagnetic wave. In Fig. 51 the

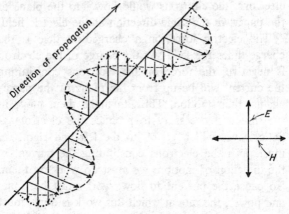

Figure 51

wave is traveling away from us, up and to the right, with the velocity of light. The vertical arrows represent the direction and strength of the electric field; the horizontal arrows represent the direction and strength of the magnetic field. The electric and magnetic fields are, of course, always at right angles to one another and to the direction of propagation. As the wave travels, we can imagine the whole pattern of arrows moving in the direction of propagation with the velocity of light, so that at any point in space the electric and magnetic fields vary sinusoidally with time as well as with distance.

Polarized Waves

We say that the wave of Fig. 51 is *vertically polarized*, because the electric field points up or down (and the magnetic field is horizontal). Of course, we can also have *horizontally polarized* waves in which the electric field is horizontal and the magnetic field vertical.

Further, we can combine such waves. Suppose, for instance, we combine horizontally and vertically polarized waves of equal field strengths so that the horizontally polarized wave lags just a quarter of a wavelength behind the vertically polarized wave. Then the electric field will first be up, then to the left, then down, then to the right, and so on. In fact, both the electric and magnetic fields, which will always be normal to the direction of propagation and to one another, will be constant in amplitude, and will change only in direction with time and distance.

Fig. 52 shows arrows representing the electric field of a *circularly polarized wave*. The heads of the arrows lie along a *helix* (like a door spring or a corkscrew). There must of course be right-handed circularly polarized waves, in which the helix is like an ordinary screw thread or corkscrew, and left-handed circularly polarized waves, corresponding to a corkscrew made so that you would have to turn it counterclockwise in order to get it into a cork.

Radio broadcasting stations send out vertically polarized waves from tall towers that act as antennas. In this country FM and TV antennas are so oriented that they send out and receive horizontally polarized waves, but in England TV waves are vertically po-

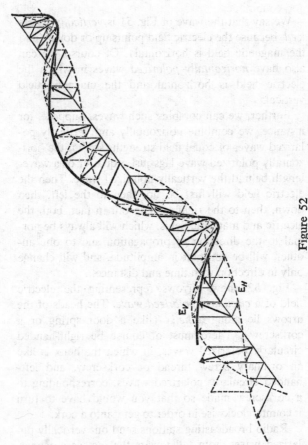

E_V

E_H

Figure 52

larized. Microwave radio relay systems make use of both polarizations. And, circular polarization is used for communication satellites in order that there will be no problem of lining up the electric field of the ground antenna with the electric field of the satellite antenna.

Maxwell's equations cover not merely electromagnetic waves but all phenomena involving electric and magnetic fields, and by studying them one can gain a general insight into the behavior of electric and magnetic fields.

For instance, imagine the slightly curved surface discussed in connection with Fig. 48 to swell out into a balloon, with the line l bounding a hole in the balloon. Let us now make the perimeter l shorter and shorter, so that finally its length becomes zero and the hole in the surface vanishes. As we do this, the line integral around l becomes smaller and smaller so that finally

$$\oint H_l dl = 0$$
$$\oint E_l dl = 0$$

We now have a *closed surface* enclosing a volume of space. What do Maxwell's equations say about such a closed surface?

The first equation says that:

$$\frac{\partial \phi}{\partial t} + I_c = 0$$

$$\frac{\partial \phi}{\partial t} = -I_c$$

This means that the total current flow, displacement plus convection current, into or out of any volume is always zero.

Gauss's Law

Imagine that we start out with no current, no electric field, and no flux. We then let a convection current, a current of electric charges, flow into the volume through the surface enclosing it. If the flow consists of positive charges, this will constitute a negative convection current, for the direction of current flow is opposite to the direction of the line normal to the surface, which points outward. Thus, according to the equation given, the flow of positive charges into the volume should produce a positive flux. The negative convection current is the rate at which positive charge crosses the surface and enters the enclosed volume; it is the rate of change of charge in the volume. $\partial \phi / \partial t$ is the rate of change of flux crossing the surface. Because, according to Maxwell's equations, the two rates of change, of charge and of flux, must be equal, by the time a total electric charge Q has flowed through the surface and into the volume, we will find that the total electric flux outward is always

$$\phi = Q$$

This is known as Gauss's law. It was known in Maxwell's time, and, like much earlier knowledge, it is embedded in Maxwell's equations. It tells how electric fields are associated with charges.

Sometimes we deal with *static* electric and magnetic fields—that is, with fields which do not change with time. For such fields, $\partial \phi / \partial t$ and $\partial \psi / \partial t$ are zero. When ϕ and ψ do not change, the only electric fields are those associated with charges, according to

Gauss's law (that is, according to Maxwell's equations).

We can deduce the inverse-square law of force between fixed charges from Maxwell's equations. Imagine a single charge Q, located in the center of a spherical surface of radius r. The electric field will have a constant strength E_1 over the surface of the sphere and will everywhere point outward. Thus, the electric flux ϕ across the surface of the sphere will be ϵE_1 times the area of the surface, or

$$\phi = 4\pi r^2 \epsilon E_1$$

According to Gauss's law

$$4\pi r^2 \epsilon E_1 = Q_1$$

$$E_1 = \frac{Q_1}{4\pi \epsilon r^2}$$

Imagine another charge of charge Q_2 to be at a distance r from the first charge. The force f exerted on Q_2 by Q_1 will be the field E_1 due to Q_1 times Q_2; thus,

$$f = \frac{Q_1 Q_2}{4\pi \epsilon r^2}$$

Thus, we have obtained the inverse-square law of force between two charges from Maxwell's equations. Like charges are repelled; unlike charges are attracted.

We are also in a position now to *prove* the assertion made in Chapter Two that in an electrostatic field the same work is done in moving a charged particle from one point to another, regardless of the path taken between the points. Now, the work done on a charge q when it moves a distance dl is just

$$qE_l dl$$

Here E_l is the component of electric field in the direction of l. If the charge moves around any closed curve, the total work is

$$q \oint E_l dl$$

But, in the case of static fields, $\partial \psi / \partial t = 0$ and the line integral is zero.

Consider the situation in Fig. 53, in which we move a charge from a to b via any one of three paths, 1, 2, or 3, and then back to a via path 4. The total work done is zero in each case. Hence, the work

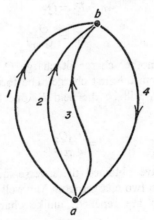

Figure 53

done in moving the charge from a to b must in each case be equal to the negative of the work done in moving the charge from b to a via path 4, regardless of what path we take from a to b.

Maxwell's equations can be applied to a multitude of general and special problems. Mathematicians, physicists and engineers often use them in what is called the *differential* form. For instance, here are Maxwell's equations in the differential form in rectangular coordinates for fields and currents which vary sinusoidally with time:

$$\frac{\partial E_z}{\partial y} - \frac{\partial E_y}{\partial z} = -j\omega\mu H_x \qquad \frac{\partial H_z}{\partial y} - \frac{\partial H_y}{\partial z} = j\omega\epsilon E_x + J_x$$

$$\frac{\partial E_x}{\partial z} - \frac{\partial E_z}{\partial x} = -j\omega\mu H_y \qquad \frac{\partial H_x}{\partial z} - \frac{\partial H_z}{\partial x} = j\omega\epsilon E_y + J_y$$

$$\frac{\partial E_y}{\partial x} - \frac{\partial E_x}{\partial y} = -j\omega\mu H_z \qquad \frac{\partial H_y}{\partial x} - \frac{\partial H_x}{\partial y} = j\omega\epsilon E_z + J_z$$

I think that the reader will understand why I will say no more about these equations.

Rather, I propose to make a few general observations which will be important to us in understanding qualitatively the operation of several important electromagnetic devices to be discussed in the next chapter.

One vital matter is the behavior of electromagnetic waves in the vicinity of conductors. As we noted in Chapter Three, electric fields cannot exist in conductors, except the very weak fields associated with the flow of current. Steady or slowly varying magnetic fields can exist inside of a conductor. When the magnetic fields vary, however, they produce electric fields which cause currents to flow, and if the variation is rapid, these currents produce a magnetic field which almost completely cancels any magnetic field inside the conductor.

In fact, radio waves scarcely penetrate conductors

at all. What they do is cause a current, a flow of electric charge, in a very thin region near the surface of the conductor. The charge distribution this flow produces at the ends of the electric lines of force, which are always normal to the surface of the conductor, is just sufficient to satisfy Maxwell's equations in the form of Gauss's law—to make possible an electric field outside the conductor and no electric field inside the conductor. Just outside the surface of a conductor the magnetic field is always parallel to the surface. And, as the charges move parallel to the surface, they constitute just enough current to satisfy Maxwell's second equation with a magnetic field parallel to the surface outside the conductor and no magnetic field inside the conductor.

The effect is that conductors reflect electromagnetic waves, just as a mirror reflects light. In fact, a mirror reflects light because the thin coating of silver on its back *is* a conductor and light *is* an electromagnetic wave. But a rough conductor, like aluminum with a matte finish, scatters light instead of reflecting it like a mirror. What do we mean by rough? We find a clue in the discussion of waves in Chapter Five. If the unevenness of the surface of a conductor is small compared with a wavelength, the conductor will reflect electromagnetic waves *specularly* (as a mirror does). The reflectors of great telescopes like that at Mount Palomar must be very smooth indeed, because the wavelength of light is so very short. The parabolic reflectors used as antennas in microwave radio systems need not be nearly so smooth or accurately shaped, because the length of microwaves is so much greater than the length of light waves.

The Constants ϵ and μ

We have not discussed one other very important matter which we cannot afford to pass over: that is, that the constants ϵ and μ are different for different substances.

ϵ is greater for glass, mica or other solid dielectrics than it is for air. Thus, the application of a given voltage across a given thickness and area of mica produces more electric flux than does the application of the same voltage across the same area and thickness of air. A change of the voltage produces more displacement current in the case of mica than in the case of air. For a given spacing between plates of a given size, a capacitor using mica as a dielectric will have more capacitance than a capacitor using air as a dielectric.

μ is much greater for iron than for air. Thus, a current through a coil wound around a closed loop of iron produces more magnetic flux than if the same coil were just in air. This is why iron cores are used in electromagnets and in transformers.

The behavior of electric and magnetic fields in spaces partly filled with dielectric materials or partly filled with magnetic materials is quite complicated, and we will consider only one case here. That is the case of lenses made of dielectric substances and surrounded by air.

The velocity of an electromagnetic wave is $1/\sqrt{\mu\epsilon}$. Thus, light waves or radio waves travel slower in a dielectric substance such as glass than they do in air or in vacuum. We have seen in Chapter Five that lenses focus waves by means of such a difference in wave velocity. A lens for focusing electromagnetic waves is an example of the utility of partly filling a space in which waves travel with a material having a dielectric constant different from that of air or vacuum.

Actually, saying that ϵ or μ is different for some substance than it is for vacuum is only a sort of average way of talking about the substance. All matter is mostly vacuum, thinly populated with minute particles such as electrons and protons. Some of these particles inherently have magnetic and electric fields associated with them. Electrons have an electric field associated with them, and they produce magnetic fields as they move within atoms.

When an electromagnetic wave travels through a substance, it moves or it changes the motions of the particles in the atoms, or of atoms or molecules themselves. Thus it affects the electric and magnetic fields of the particles or of the atoms or molecules. When the waves are long and smooth compared with the spacings between the particles, atoms, or molecules, we can take these effects into account by assigning to the substance a value of ϵ or μ different from ϵ or μ for the vacuum of which the solid is largely composed.

Microwave radio offers a beautiful analogy to such behavior. When we shoot a radio wave through a regularly spaced array of metal disks or strips, spaced close together compared with the wavelength, the wave is not reflected or scattered. Instead, it behaves just as if it were passing through a substance with a value of ϵ higher than that for air or vacuum. The fields of the wave move charges about on the metal disks or strips, and the fields of these moving charges mimic on a large scale the behavior of the submicroscopic molecules of glass when a light wave passes through the glass.

Chapter Seven

SOME USEFUL ELECTROMAGNETIC DEVICES

Maxwell's equations serve as a tool for understanding and calculating the behavior of a large number of useful devices, and as an inspiration to the invention of new devices. While we can scarcely discuss the behavior of many of these devices quantitatively, we can see qualitatively how some of them work.

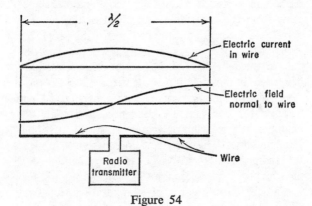

Figure 54

As one example, it can be shown that an electromagnetic wave tends to travel along a thin wire at about the speed of light. If the wire is half a wavelength long, the reflections at the ends will cause a standing wave pattern similar to that of the vibrating string in Fig. 40. This situation is illustrated in Fig. 54. Power from a radio transmitter connected at the center of the wire causes the current flow in the wire, and this current is very nearly sinusoidal in its distribution along the wire. As shown, the current is largest at the center and zero at the ends. There is also an electric field at the surface of the wire, and this field is, of course, normal to the surface. This electric field is largest at the ends of the wire and zero at the center.

Antennas

The current in the wire produces an electromagnetic wave in a manner quite analogous to that described in connection with Fig. 51. Some distance away from the wire the electric field of this wave is parallel to the wire and the magnetic field circles the wire. The wave is strongest in a direction perpendicular to the wire, and is weaker in other directions, being zero in the direction of the wire.

Half-wave antennas such as that of Fig. 54 can be used for FM and TV reception, and some TV antennas are made up of *arrays* of several such half-wave antennas. This arrangement is designed to make the radiation and the response to radiation great in some desired direction in which the array is "pointed." In the words of Chapter Five, an array of many elements is used to produce a narrow beam of waves.

In radio broadcast transmission the polarization is vertical. Moreover, the wavelength is long—around

300 meters or 1000 feet. It is common practice to use a quarter-wave vertical antenna as shown in Fig. 55. The ground about the antenna acts as a con-

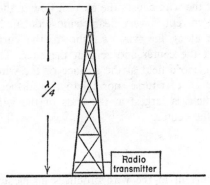

Figure 55

ductor. Ordinarily, wires or metal mesh are put under or on the ground for some distance around the antenna to assure sufficient conductivity near the antenna.

We remember that a conductor reflects electromagnetic waves. In effect, the quarter-wave antenna of Fig. 55 sees a reflection of itself in the conducting ground, and it radiates just as does the half-wave antenna of Fig. 54. Of course, there is really no electromagnetic wave under the ground, any more than what you see in a mirror really exists behind the mirror.

Wires can be formed into other shapes and used as antennas. One such shape is a helix or coil, as shown in Fig. 56. If the diameter of the helix is great enough (in terms of the wavelength), it radiates a

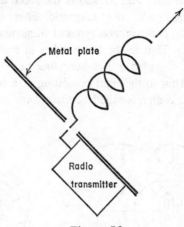

Figure 56

circularly polarized wave, directed along the axis of the helix, in the direction shown by the arrow. But if the circumference of the helix is small compared with a half wavelength, a long helix will guide an electromagnetic wave without causing any radiation. The wave will travel along the wire at very nearly the speed of light. The fields of the wave will move along the axis more slowly. If it takes 10 feet of wire to wind one foot of helix, the speed of the wave along the axis will be about a tenth the speed of light. Small helices of this sort are used in amplifying tubes called *traveling-wave tubes*.

This brings us to the matter of conveying or guiding electromagnetic waves from one point to another —from a radio transmitter to an antenna, for instance, or from an antenna to a radio receiver. Any two parallel conductors close to one another form a *transmission line.* Fig. 57 shows the electric lines of force (solid) and the magnetic lines of force (dashed) for two common types of transmission line, seen end-on. That to the left consists of two parallel wires, and is called a *two-wire line* or a *parallel-wire line.* That to the right consisting of a tube with a wire at the center, is called a *coaxial line.*

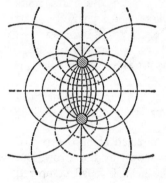
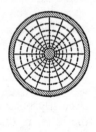

Figure 57

Near the surface of the conductors (wires, tubes) the electric field is everywhere normal to the surface and the magnetic field is everywhere parallel to the surface, as is true for all microwave fields near the surface of conductors, and neither electric nor magnetic fields are present inside of conductors.

But in comparatively recent years (more or less since World War II) a quite different medium for guiding electromagnetic waves has come into wide use. The work of Southworth and Barrow has shown us that if the waves are short enough they will go through a metal pipe or tube called a waveguide.

Usually, less power is lost because of electrical resistance in a waveguide than in a transmission line of the same length. However, waves have to be short compared with the diameter of the tube to go through a waveguide. Waveguides are usually either rectangular or round in cross section. They are used extensively in radar and in microwave communication systems.

For instance, in the transcontinental radio relay system, which sends telephone and television signals across the country, the antennas are built on the tops of towers, some of them over a hundred feet high, while the transmitters and receivers are installed on the ground. Long rectangular or circular metal tubes or waveguides carry the signals from the transmitter to the transmitting antenna and from the receiving antenna to the receiver with little loss.

The Uses of Resonators

Another extremely important electromagnetic device is an enclosure or *resonator* which can support a trapped electromagnetic wave of some particular frequency, the *resonant frequency*, of the resonator. We have seen in Chapter Five, and particularly in connection with Fig. 43, how such a device can be used to pass signals of some desired narrow range of frequencies and to reject signals of other frequencies. A resonator can be made of a length of two-wire or coaxial transmission line by connecting the two conductors together at each end. Or, a resonator can be made of a length of waveguide by covering the ends of the tubular waveguide with metal plates. Holes in the plates let electromagnetic waves in and out, for the sort of electrical filter described in connection with Fig. 43.

Sometimes resonators are made in particular shapes for special purposes. Fig. 58 shows one such resonator in cross section. It is a shell of metal with a more or less doughnut shape, but there is a thin slit or gap extending around the inside of the hole of the doughnut. It is chiefly across this gap that the electric field of the electromagnetic wave appears, as indicated by the lines of force with arrowheads. The

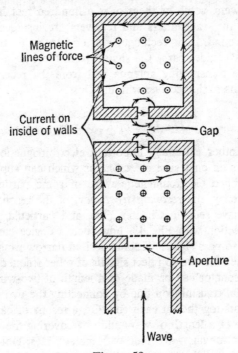

Figure 58

magnetic lines of force are closed circles winding around inside the doughnut. In the figure we see them pointed toward us in the upper part of the cross section and away from us in the lower part. On the inside surface of the walls a current flows, as indicated. There are, of course, no electric or magnetic fields inside the metal of the resonator.

Both the electric and the magnetic fields vary sinusoidally with time. The change in the magnetic field produces the electric field, and the change in the electric field produces the magnetic field, in accord with Maxwell's equations. Thus, when the strength of the magnetic field is least, when it is changing most rapidly in passing from negative to positive, the electric field is greatest. When the rate of change in electric field is greatest, when the electric field is passing from negative to positive and is zero, the magnetic field is greatest. This inverse relation is characteristic of the standing wave in a resonator and different from a wave traveling through space. We may remember that in a plane electromagnetic wave the electric field is greatest when the magnetic field is greatest, while we see that in the resonator the electric field is greatest when the magnetic field is zero.

A trapped wave dies out as it oscillates unless power is supplied continually. In Fig. 58 the power is supplied as a wave traveling through a metal pipe or waveguide and is admitted to the resonator through a small aperture.

A resonator of the sort shown in Fig. 58 is used in vacuum tube oscillators and amplifiers called *klystrons* in order to slow down or speed up electrons in an electron beam shot through the gap, or to take energy from the convection current in an electron beam. In the resonators of vacuum tubes the inside of the resonator may be evacuated, and the aperture in the waveguide may be covered with glass, mica, or ceramic.

A resonator, we can see, is a very useful device for filtering out a signal of one range of frequencies from other signals, or for producing a strong electric field to act on a beam of electrons. We see also that the size of a resonator is always comparable to the wavelength of the electromagnetic wave it is tuned to, though usually the largest dimension of the resonator is substantially less than a wavelength. This is all right for a wavelength of 3 centimeters (a frequency of 10,000,000,000 cycles per second) or for a wavelength of 10 centimeters (a frequency of 3,000,000,000 cycles per second), but what about a wavelength of 300 meters (a frequency of 1,000,000 cycles per second)? Clearly, a resonator of the sort we have described is impractical for such frequencies. Over wide ranges of frequency we use *resonant circuits* made up of coils called *inductors* and devices called *capacitors*. Each of these has an interest in itself.

We can apply Maxwell's equations to the production of a magnetic field by a current, as discussed in connection with Fig. 21 of Chapter Four. This figure has been redrawn in Fig. 59 and a closed line *l* has been drawn through the solenoid for a length *L* and back on the outside.

The wire carries a steady convection current of *I* amperes. If the coil has *n* turns per meter, the current flows through the boundary l a total of nL times. According to Maxwell's first equation, then

$$\oint H_l dl = nLI$$

Now, the magnetic field has a nearly constant value H inside the solenoid and a very small value outside the solenoid. Hence, the line integral is simply HL, and we have

$$HL = nLI$$
$$H = nI$$

This is the expression for the magnetic field inside a long solenoid. The strength of the field is equal to the *ampere turns per meter*.

In Fig. 59 the battery is necessary simply to cause the electric current to persist in spite of the electrical resistance of the wire, which causes electric energy to be turned into heat just as mechanical friction turns the kinetic energy of motion into heat. In an *ideal* coil, the wire would have no resistance. Let us consider the behavior of such an ideal coil.

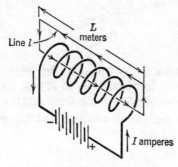

Figure 59

Maxwell's second equation tells us that

$$\oint E_1 dl = -\frac{\partial \psi}{\partial t}$$

That is, if we go along any path circling magnetic flux, the integral of electric field along the path times distance along the path is equal to the rate of change of the magnetic flux. Now suppose that in Fig. 60 we take the path through the wire and circle around the flux N times, and then go across the gap between the ends of the wire to complete the closed path. As the wire is a perfect conductor, there can be no elec-

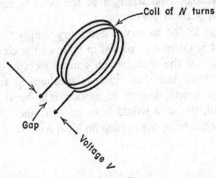

Figure 60

tric field along the part of the path inside the wire. Thus, all the electric field must appear between the ends of the wire. We call the line integral of the field between the ends, or *terminals*, of the wire the voltage V. We then have

$$V = N\oint E_1 dl = N\frac{\partial \psi}{\partial t}$$

What will happen if we make the voltage V between the ends of the wire have some specified constant value by connecting an ideal lossless battery of voltage V between the ends of the wire? The rate of change of the magnetic flux ψ must assume some constant value $\partial\psi/\partial t$ such that the equation is satisfied. That is, the magnetic flux and the current in the coil, which is proportional to the magnetic flux, must both increase with time at a constant rate; both the current and the flux will be proportional to time.

This reminds us very much of the behavior of a mass acted on by a force. According to Newton's laws of motion, a constant force acting on a mass causes the velocity of the mass to increase at a constant rate or acceleration, so that the velocity of the mass is proportional to time. In fact, there is a close analogy between the laws of electric circuits and the laws of motion. We can liken voltage to force, and current to velocity. As an analog of mass, we have the *inductance* of a coil or inductor. The inductance is the flux per ampere of current times the number of turns.

The flow of current in a coil is like the sliding of a mass on a slippery surface. The resistance of an actual (as opposed to an ideal) coil is like the friction of the sliding mass.

Capacitors and Inductors

Coils or inductors are one of the building blocks of radio. Another building block is what is called a *capacitor* or a *condenser*. This device is just two metal plates very close together, separated either by air or by an insulating solid material. Fig. 61 shows

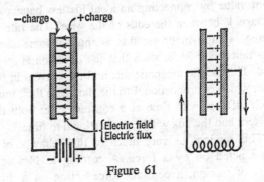

Figure 61

two such metal plates connected by a battery, which produces an electric field and an electric flux between them.* By Gauss's law, this flux is associated with charges on the surfaces of the conductors. If the total flux is ϕ, there is a charge $Q = +\phi$ on the positive plate of the condenser and a charge $Q = -\phi$ on the negative plate of the condenser. The voltage V across the capacitor is related to the electric field E between the plates. If the field is constant between the plates and if the distance between the plates is l, then

$$V = El$$

For a given capacitor, the charge Q is proportional to the voltage V; that is, Q is equal to V multiplied by a constant C:

$$Q = CV$$

* In this figure the arrowheads are drawn in the direction of the electric field, and not in the direction of the force on an electron, as in Chapter Three.

The constant C is called the *capacitance* of the capacitor.

We note that if we make no electrical connections to the plates of a capacitor, so that the charge Q cannot flow away but must remain constant, then V will vary if C varies. We can change the capacitance C by changing the distance l between the plates. This is the principle of the condenser microphone. In this device, a thin stretched piece of metal foil is placed very close to a solid metal plate and a charge is put on the resulting capacitor. Sound waves cause the thin foil to vibrate. Vibration changes the distance between plate and foil and thus changes the capacitance and so the voltage across the capacitor, producing an electric signal which corresponds to the sound wave striking the foil.

Usually, capacitors (condensers) have unmoving plates and constant capacitances and are used for other purposes. Consider, for instance, what would happen if we removed the battery of Fig. 61 and connected the plates of the same capacitor together by means of a wire, as shown in Fig. 61. A current would tend to flow from the positive plate to the negative plate. Suppose, however, that the wire was coiled, to form an inductor. It would take some time for the current to start flowing. Further, once the current got started in the coil, it would be hard to stop. As a matter of fact, the current would oscillate back and forth sinusoidally in the coil, alternately charging the plates of the capacitor minus and plus, and then, later, plus and minus. The behavior of the current is like the oscillations of a mass supported by a spring. The capacitor is analogous to the spring.

This behavior is also like that of an electromagnetic wave trapped in a closed box or resonator, that is, a standing wave. It should be, for both are governed by the same laws—that is, Maxwell's equations.

When in microwave radio we want to let signals of certain frequencies pass and to reject signals of other frequencies, we use, as already noted, a closed box or resonator, with holes to let waves in and out, and the signal to and from the resonator travels as electromagnetic waves in tubes or waveguides. At lower frequencies it is more convenient to send signals along wire, or transmission lines, and to obtain a behavior analogous to that of the resonator by use of circuits made up of coils and capacitors. Thus, when you turn the dial of your radio, you actually are adjusting the "resonator," which consists of a coil and a capacitor. Usually, it is the capacitor which is adjusted. This capacitor consists of interleaved metal plates with an air space between, and the degree of interleaving is changed as the knob turns the shaft. This changes the *resonant frequency* of the electrical circuit consisting of the coil and capacitor.

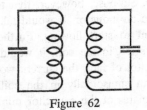

Figure 62

Sometimes two resonant circuits are *coupled* by placing the coils close enough together so that the change in magnetic flux in one induces a voltage in the other. Such a pair of resonant circuits is represented in Fig. 62. Such *double-tuned* circuits are often used to couple vacuum tubes or transistors together in radio-frequency amplifiers.

The fraction of the signal power transmitted through a single-tuned resonant circuit varies with the frequency of the signal as shown in the left of Fig. 63, with a maximum transmission at the resonant frequency of the circuit, f_o. For a double-tuned circuit the curve of power transmitted vs. signal fre-

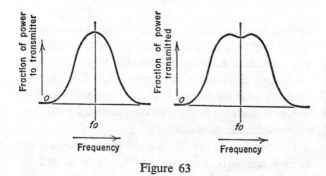

Figure 63

quency has a flatter top, as shown in the right of Fig. 63.

Transformers and Their Uses

One extremely simple and useful electromagnetic device is a *transformer*. A transformer consists of two coils of wire wound around a closed *core* of magnetic material, as shown in Fig. 64. The cores of transformers may be made of thin sheets or *lamina-*

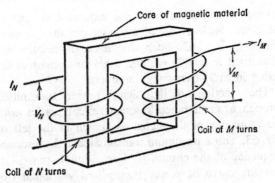

Figure 64

tions of alloys of iron and other elements, alloys that have a high magnetic permeability. The thin laminations are insulated from one another to avoid closed conducting paths in which current could flow. Sometimes transformer cores are made of ceramics called *ferrites* which are electrically nonconducting but have a high magnetic permeability.

The permeability of the core of the transformer is so high compared with that of the space around it that the magnetic flux which the currents in the coils produce in the core is far greater than the flux produced in the air outside the core. We can say quite accurately that the total flux passing through each coil is ψ, the flux in the core. Thus, if one coil has N turns, the voltage V_N between its terminals will be:

$$V_N = N \frac{\partial \psi}{\partial t}$$

while the voltage between the terminals of the coil with M turns, V_M, will be

$$V_M = M \frac{\partial \psi}{\partial t}$$

and

$$\frac{V_N}{V_M} = \frac{N}{M}$$

A transformer changes a signal of one voltage into a signal of another voltage, in a ratio depending on the turns ratio. It also changes a signal of one current into a signal of another current.

The currents in the two coils of a transformer flow in such directions that they tend to produce flux in opposite directions. In a good transformer the current required to produce the flux is a very small fraction of the current in either coil. Hence, the magnetizing effects of each coil (that is, the current times the number of turns) must be nearly the same. Very nearly

$$NI_N = MI_M$$

$$\frac{I_N}{I_M} = \frac{M}{N}$$

If the current rises to its peak at the same time as the voltage, the power supplied at the input of the transformer is

$$P_N = V_N I_N$$

From these relations we see that the output power is very nearly

$$P_M = V_M I_M = V_N \left(\frac{M}{N}\right) I_N \left(\frac{N}{M}\right) = V_N I_N$$

The power output from a good transformer is very nearly equal to the power input, but the output voltage and current can be quite different from the input voltage and current.

Transformers are used to reduce the voltage from high tension (high voltage) transmission lines to the 110 volts used in your home. They are used also in interconnecting transistors and vacuum tubes in radio and other electronic circuits, and for many other purposes in the field of electronics.

Chapter Eight

SIGNALS

So far, in discussing electromagnetic waves we have talked about waves that vary sinusoidally with time and with distance. We have seen that the velocity is the wavelength times the frequency. We have considered standing waves in resonators or resonant circuits, in which the fields, the voltage, and the current vary sinusoidally with time.

Sinusoidal waves, waves with a single frequency, can be transmitted, received, and amplified. They are, however, rather uninteresting. Unlike the sorts of signals we actually send by TV or radio or hear over the telephone, sine waves are endlessly repetitious. A single sine wave can never tell us anything new; it conveys no information.

Fourier Series

But sine waves are important because, as we have noted, sine waves preserve their shape, their unique sort of variation with time, in passing through any linear system. If this were the only property of sine waves, they would perhaps be mere mathematical curiosities. Sine waves have another very important property, however, which was clearly demonstrated by Baron Jean Baptiste Joseph Fourier, an early nineteenth-century French mathematician and physicist. Any reasonable physical curve, any reasonable variation of a field, a voltage, a current, with time, can be represented as a sum of sine waves! And, by *reasonable*, I merely exclude certain pathological mathematical specimens, largely invented to show that Fourier's efforts to reduce everything to a sum of sine waves can be frustrated by one sufficiently ingenious.

The representation by *Fourier series* and *Fourier integrals* of any electrical signal as a combination of sine waves has a profound importance in electronics. The behavior of a linear circuit, such as a resonator, a capacitor, an inductor, a resistor, or a complicated combination of these elements, can be calculated easily if the applied signal is a sine wave. If the input signal to any linear circuit or amplifier is a combination of sine waves of various frequencies, the output will be a combination of sine waves of the same frequencies. In dealing with the total signal, each *sinusoidal component* of the signal can be treated separately.

The representation of signals by sine waves of several frequencies is so important, so fundamental to the electronic art, that we must have some understanding of it. Such understanding can be achieved most easily by considering a few simple examples. For instance, Fig. 65 shows at the top two sine waves of slightly different frequencies, f_1 and f_2, and at the bottom the sum of the two sine waves. The signal at the bottom is a signal which has components of two frequencies only. In general appearance it is a

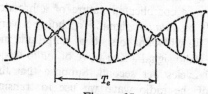

Figure 65

wavy signal whose amplitude varies with time. A dotted line has been drawn outlining this combined signal; this curve is called the *envelope* of the signal. The envelope rises from zero to a greatest value and falls to zero again in some time T_e which is indicated in the figure, and this rise and fall is repeated with a frequency, f_e, given by

$$f_e = \frac{1}{T_e}$$

Always,

$$f_e = f_1 - f_2$$

That is, the frequency with which the envelope rises and falls is the difference between the frequencies of the two sine waves of which the signal is made up, the greater frequency minus the lesser frequency.

AM and FM Signals

The signal shown at the bottom of Fig. 65 resembles somewhat the sort of signal sent out by an AM, that is, *amplitude modulation*, radio transmitter (a broadcast transmitter, for instance), but it is really not the same. Let us try to understand the slightly more complicated nature of a broadcast or *amplitude modulation* signal. To choose a very simple case, we will want to send by amplitude modulation of a radio signal a sine wave of audio frequency, say, 500 cycles per second. Suppose that the frequency of the radio wave we use to transmit the signal is 1,000,000 cycles.

At the broadcast transmitter, the sine wave of 1,000,000 cycles frequency is put into a device called a *modulator*. By means of the modulator the 500-cycle sine wave controls the amplitude or envelope of the 1,000,000-cycle sine wave, so that the envelope is itself a 500-cycle sine wave, as shown in Fig. 66. (Here the frequency of the radio-frequency wave is not to scale.)

When we receive such a signal with a radio receiver, we can recover the 500-cycle sine wave by means of a *detector*. A detector is a rectifier such as our diode of Fig. 12 of Chapter Three, a device which passes current in only one direction. If we put the AM signal of Fig. 66 through such a rectifier followed by a filter which will pass audio frequencies only, we will get out a unidirectional current of varying strength. In fact, the strength of this current will vary just as does the sinusoidal envelope of the AM signal.

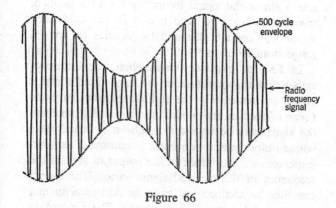

500 cycle
envelope

Radio
frequency
signal

Figure 66

While we can think of an AM signal such as that shown in Fig. 66 as a sine wave with a varying amplitude, strictly speaking a sine wave can be a sine wave only if it has a constant amplitude. If the amplitude varies, several frequencies must be present. As a matter of fact, when we modulate a sine wave of frequency f so as to obtain a signal with a sinusoidal envelope of some frequency f_e, we find that the signal we get contains not only a component of frequency f called the *carrier* but also two *sidebands* having frequencies $f + f_e$ and $f - f_e$.

In general, the signals we want to transmit by radio are not simple sine waves; they are combinations of sine waves of many frequencies. A telephone signal contains frequencies lying between 200 and 3500 cycles. A high fidelity *audio* or sound signal may embrace a band of frequencies of perhaps twenty to 20,000 cycles. A TV signal requires a band of about four megacycles. In general, if we amplitude-modulate a sinusoidal signal frequency f with a band of frequencies lying between 0 and B, the modulated signal will contain sideband frequencies covering a range from $f - B$ to $f + B$.

In FM, or *frequency modulation*, the frequency rather than the amplitude of the transmitted signal is varied in modulating the radio-frequency wave. In order to recover the modulation in an FM receiver, the signal can be passed through an electrical filter whose output varies with input frequency. This filtering causes the amplitude of the output to vary as the frequency of the received signal varies. The output can then be rectified just as in an AM receiver and so the modulation can be recovered. There are other ways of recovering the modulation from an FM signal.

In amplitude-modulating a signal, there is a limit to the allowable degree of modulation. If we increase the strength of the modulating signal, eventually a level of modulation of the radio-frequency sine wave will be reached such that the amplitude of the radio-frequency signal will at some time fall to zero. If we try to modulate the sine wave more strongly than this, the envelope will no longer accurately reproduce the modulating signal. Hence, at the radio receiver, the modulating signal cannot be accurately reproduced.

There is no similar limitation in FM, but increasing the strength of the modulation does have an effect. Suppose that the carrier frequency is f and the modulating signal is a sine wave of frequency f_e. If the modulation is weak, it can be shown that the only new frequencies produced are sidebands of frequencies $f - f_e$ and $f + f_e$. If the modulation is stronger, however, one finds that other frequencies, such as $f - 3f_e$, $f - 2f_e$, $f + 2f_e$, $f + 3f_e$ are produced. An FM signal may cover a very broad band of frequencies, much broader than the band of frequencies of the modulating signal.

We should take note of one feature which is common to the fluctuation of the envelope of two sine waves, as shown in Fig. 65; to the AM signal of Fig. 66; and to the FM signal as well. Regardless of the actual frequencies involved, it is the difference of frequencies, the band of frequencies, which determines the fluctuation of the envelope, and which is determined by the modulating signal applied to the radio-frequency signal in AM and FM. In fact, the frequencies comprising a signal can be shifted, all by a constant amount, and the important features of the signal will be preserved in the process.

In a sense, this is what is done in radio and TV broadcasting. Each radio program starts out as audio frequencies lying in the same frequency range. Different radio stations send these signals to us by means of radio waves of different frequencies. The radio antenna picks up all the different radio programs, but, as different programs have been sent as radio waves of different frequencies, electrical filters in the radio set can select the radio frequencies corresponding to one program and reject the frequencies corresponding to other programs.

AM (amplitude modulation) and FM (frequency modulation) are two rather specialized ways by means of which a signal of one frequency (an audio signal) can be represented by a signal of another frequency (a radio signal). In AM, if the audio signal is a 500-cycle sine wave, the radio signal representing it will comprise a signal of carrier frequency and two sidebands having frequencies 500 cycles above and below the carrier frequency. An FM signal may be even more complicated.

Frequency Shifting

However, in representing a signal of one frequency by a signal of another, it is possible simply to shift the frequency of the original signal, so that for each frequency in the original signal there is just one frequency in the signal which represents it. This is important for several purposes. Much as in radio and TV broadcasting, the frequencies of signals may be shifted so that several different signals can be sent without confusion along one transmission line, or through one broad-band amplifier, each having been shifted to a different band of frequencies. There are other uses for frequency shifting, too. For instance, it is often desirable to change the frequency of a signal for greater convenience in amplifying it; we will come to this use of frequency shifting in due time.

We cannot go into all the details of frequency shifting, but I believe that a simple case will illustrate the phenomenon involved. Suppose that we add to a weak signal of frequency f_1 (a of Fig. 67) a strong signal of frequency f_2 (b of Fig. 67). The combined signal (c of Fig. 67) superficially resembles an amplitude-modulation signal. The frequency of the envelope (shown dashed in Fig. 67) is $f_2 - f_1$. This frequency is not present in the simple sum of the two signals, c of Fig. 67, but if we put this combined signal through a non-linear device called a *mixer*, or

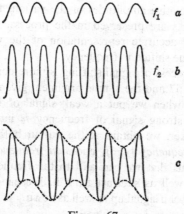

Figure 67

a *frequency converter*, or a *modulator*, the frequency of the envelope, $f_2 - f_1$, will appear in the output and can be filtered out. The process is analogous to the detection of an AM signal, which we discussed earlier. If f_1 is greater than f_2, we still get the difference frequency, which is $f_1 - f_2$. This overall process is sometimes called *beating* the two signals, and the frequency $f_1 - f_2$ (or $f_2 - f_1$) is called the *beat frequency*.

When a weak and a much stronger signal are passed through a non-linear device (mixer, frequency converter, modulator), the amplitude of the difference frequency signal in the output of the mixer will be proportional to the amplitude of the weak signal; the frequency converter is in this sense a linear device. Because of this linearity, when the weak signal consists not of a single frequency component but of many frequency components, each component is separately shifted in frequency by a constant amount, and the relative amplitudes of the various frequency components are preserved in the process. Thus, we obtain an accurate representation of the weak signal, but one shifted in frequency.

This process of signal shifting is more complicated than Fig. 67 and the simple argument given disclose. Actually, when we put a weak signal of frequency f_1 and a strong signal of frequency f_2 into a non-linear mixer, we obtain at the output both the *difference frequency* $f_2 - f_1$ and *sum frequency* $f_1 + f_2$. This means that we can add to the frequency of a signal as well as subtract from it. We can shift the frequency of a signal up as well as down.

The Superheterodyne Receiver

The principle of frequency shifting is applied in a sort of radio receiver called the *double-detection* or *superheterodyne* receiver, which is used in AM, in FM, and in microwave radio.

Fig. 68 shows the parts of a superheterodyne receiver which might be used, for instance, in receiving an AM broadcast signal. It might be tuned to receive a signal transmitted by amplitude modulating a 770-kilocycle sinusoidal wave. The received signal might contain frequencies lying in the 10-kilocycle band between 765 kilocycles and 775 kilocycles. If we put this received signal into a non-linear mixer (frequency converter, modulator) together with a strong signal having a frequency of 1235 kilocycles, we will get out a signal lying in the range 460 kilocycles to 470 kilocycles, and a signal lying in the range 2000 kilocycles to 2010 kilocycles. We can select the for-

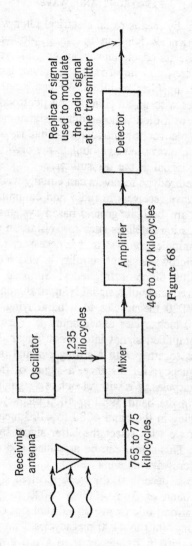

Figure 68

Receiving antenna

765 to 775 kilocycles

Oscillator

1235 kilocycles

Mixer

Amplifier

460 to 470 kilocycles

Detector

Replica of signal used to modulate the radio signal at the transmitter

mer signal by means of an electrical filter which will pass frequencies lying in the range 460–470 kilocycles. The tuned circuits in an amplifier called an *intermediate-frequency* (or IF) amplifier can in fact constitute the filter required. We can amplify these frequencies with an amplifier using pentrodes. Then, by means of a diode, the amplified signal can be detected to recover the modulation—that is, the audio signal which was used to modulate the original radio-frequency signal at the transmitter.

Superheterodyne receivers can equally well be used as microwave receivers in radio and communication, and they are both in ground-based systems and in communication satellites such as Telstar. In a microwave communication system it is necessary to receive a weak microwave signal, amplify it, and send it out at a slightly different frequency. Suppose that we shift the frequency of a signal lying in the band from 4000 to 4020 megacycles to a band lying between 60 and 80 megacycles and amplify it. We can then put this amplified signal into a non-linear device, a modulator, together with a stronger signal of microwave frequency: for instance, a signal of frequency 4020 megacycles. We will get out two signals: a signal lying in the band 3980 to 4000 megacycles and a signal lying in the band 4080 to 4100 megacycles. We can if we wish select the latter signal by means of a filter. This signal can be amplified and radiated from a microwave antenna.

In the case described, the weak received signal occupied a band of from 4000 to 4020 megacycles, while the strong microwave signal sent out occupied a band from 4080 to 4100 megacycles. The purpose of such a shift in frequency is to avoid having the output signal picked up at the input and amplified repeatedly; this would cause distortion of the signal and could result in oscillation.

In the superheterodyne receiver the signal is shifted in frequency for convenience in amplifying it. The frequency of a signal may, as we have said, be shifted for another sort of reason. For instance, a microwave radio relay system is capable of carrying hundreds of telephone conversations at once. A single telephone signal occupies a band or *channel* of frequencies from approximately 200 cycles to 3500 cycles. By frequency-shifting each telephone signal so that different telephone signals occupy different bands of frequencies (just as different broadcast stations use different bands of frequencies), a large number of telephone channels can be stacked one above another in frequency. In one typical case, a group of twelve channels is stacked into a band lying from 60,000 cycles to 108,000 cycles. Then five of these groups are shifted in frequency; and stacked above one another to occupy a band from 312,000 to 552,000 cycles; they form what is called a *super-group*, embracing a total of sixty channels. Finally, ten super-groups, totaling 600 channels, are stacked one above another in the frequency range of 64,000 to 2,788,000 cycles, to form the combined signal of 600 telephone channels, for transmission by microwave radio relay (or by other means). And, even more channels can be combined in this way.

Transmission systems such as this, in which many messages are sent simultaneously over different frequencies, are called *carrier* systems. All long-distance telephony, whether over open wires, over multiconductor cables, or over coaxial cables or submarine cables, makes use of carrier systems of one form or another. Some carrier systems accommodate only two or four channels, some a dozen; the L-3 coaxial-cable-carrier system can transmit somewhat more than 1800 telephone channels simultaneously. Always, if more channels are to be transmitted, more bandwidth is required, for each original signal must be shifted to some range of frequencies different from that used for any other signal.

Bandwidth and Pulse Length

We see that bandwidth, the range of frequencies occupied by a signal, is a very important and, we might say, a very persistent property of the signal. When the frequency is shifted, bandwidth is preserved. The bandwidth of a wire or a coaxial cable or a microwave system measures how many telephone channels can be transmitted over the system. When it comes to determining what a signal can be used for, the bandwidth is more important than the frequency, for the frequency can be shifted. So far we have considered bandwidth in connection with radio and TV signals, but bandwidth is equally important in other sorts of signals as well. In radar, for instance, the signals used are pulses, which rise and fall in amplitude over a short time. Fig. 69 illustrates a pulse. The radar sends out a series of such pulses to search for planes or ships. The pulses are reflected back by the object sought, and the distance of the object can be measured by measuring the time it takes a pulse to go out and return.

There is a fundamental law that has to do with the *duration*, or *length* (of time), of such pulses. In Fig.

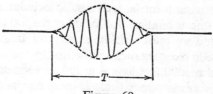

Figure 69

69, the length of the pulse is indicated by the time interval T, during which the pulse is greater than some small fraction of its maximum amplitude. The general rule is that this pulse length cannot be less than the reciprocal of the range, or band, of frequencies making up the pulse. For instance, if we use frequencies lying in the range between frequency f_1 and frequency f_2, then the band B of frequency used is

$$B = f_1 - f_2$$

In this case, the least length T that the pulse can have is

$$T = \frac{1}{B} \text{ seconds}$$

As this rule has been illustrated and stated it is, of course, approximate, but it can be formulated more exactly in mathematical terms.

This relation between pulse length and bandwidth is vitally important in radar. A radio wave travels with a velocity 3×10^8 meters per second, or, very nearly, 1000 feet in a microsecond, that is, a millionth of a second. Thus, a radar pulse whose duration is one microsecond is about 1000 feet long as it travels through the air as a microwave radar wave.

Early radars used pulses of about this duration. According to our formula, such a pulse includes a range of frequencies of about 1,000,000 cycles, or 1 megacycle, and we must amplify a range of frequencies this wide in receiving such a pulse.

A pulse 1000 feet long is a dull tool to use if we wish to sort out planes flying in close formation and to measure their distances precisely. Some modern radars use pulses having lengths of a tenth of a microsecond or less. To amplify a pulse a tenth of a microsecond long requires a ten-megacycle bandwidth.

In experimental microwave work pulses having lengths of a thousandth of a microsecond or less have been used. Such pulses are only about a foot long. What have they been used for? They have been sent down waveguides to find electrical imperfections such as bad joints and dents. Perhaps someday they will be used in communication through waveguides.

A pulse a thousandth of a microsecond long embraces a band of frequencies at least 1000 megacycles wide. Let us consider what this means. We have seen that the greater the bandwidth, the greater the number of signals, telephone, radio, or TV, that can be sent using the bandwidth. The entire broadcast range of frequencies is only about 1 megacycle wide; it extends from about .5 megacycles to 1.5 megacycles. Above this frequency lie various police and assorted communication bands. Between 10 and 30 megacycles lie all the short-wave frequencies on which transoceanic communication, both telegraph and telephone, depend. Around 50 megacycles are TV channels; a little above 100 megacycles are all our FM broadcast channels; and the rest of the TV channels, except for ultrahigh-frequency TV, extend little above 200 megacycles. If we are to amplify a pulse a thousandth of a microsecond long, we must amplify simultaneously a band of frequencies greater than that needed to send all our broadcast, short wave, FM and most of our TV channels, along with assorted other bands, military as well as civilian. And yet, bands of frequencies 1000 megacycles wide and more can be amplified by a particular type of amplifier called a traveling-wave tube. Such bands could in principle be used to transmit hundreds of thousands of telephone channels and a great many TV channels at once through waveguides, and perhaps they will be in the future.

Chapter Nine

SOME VACUUM TUBE AMPLIFIERS

The whole art of communication is the art of generating, transmitting and receiving signals of sufficient bandwidth and power to convey the messages we want to send from one place to another. And this would all be impossible without one indispensable device—an amplifier. Indeed, the whole of our complicated art of communication, control and computation is completely dependent on the existence of amplifiers which, with almost unthinkable rapidity and with sufficient fidelity, can control large amounts of power in a manner dictated by a weaker input or control signal.

The nature of any amplifier is summed up in the simple drawing of Fig. 70. The amplifier, somewhere inside the box labeled *amplifier*, does not produce power; it controls it. Thus, the amplifier must be pro-

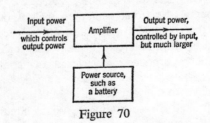

Figure 70

vided with a *power source*, from which it can draw power. An *input signal* of small power goes into the amplifier. The amplifier supplies at the *output* an *output signal* which is to some degree a replica of the input signal, but an amplified replica with greater power. The output signal may in actual cases have two times the power of the input signal, or ten times, or 100 times, or 10,000 times or more the power of the input signal, but the power must be greater than that of the input signal for the device to be an amplifier.

Uses of Amplifiers

Amplifiers are needed in long-distance telephony. Before amplifiers were available, long-distance calls were weak and uncertain. Nowadays, in its travel across the country a long-distance telephone call is amplified every three to thirty miles (depending on just how it is sent). You hear a person in a coast-to-coast call perhaps better than you hear a man in a nearby suburb. All long-distance calls are amplified.

In order to control electronically complicated machines such as lathes, steel mills, chemical plants, or airplanes, weak control signals must be amplified so that they can operate machinery.

In complex electronic computers the output of one part of the equipment must control the operation of other parts, and amplification is necessary for this.

In order to produce the electrical oscillations radiated as radio waves, an oscillator is needed. Suppose we connect the output of an amplifier back to the input through a resonator or resonant circuit tuned to a particular frequency. Initially, there will always be some small disturbance called *noise*, and this will be amplified. The greater power of the output will again be amplified, and the signal will build up to some final value. The device *oscillates*, producing a sinusoidal signal which can be used in a radio transmitter, or for many other purposes.

The Importance of Vacuum Tubes

Before the invention of the transistor, a few years ago, vacuum tubes were, if not the only amplifiers available, at least the only versatile amplifiers which could make possible a diverse and effective electronic art. For many purposes, vacuum tubes are still irreplaceable. While transistors are as yet relatively low-power devices, vacuum tubes supply steady powers of hundreds of thousands of watts and peak powers of tens of millions of watts. While transistors can act as effective amplifiers up to frequencies of several thousands of megacycles, vacuum tubes have been built which amplify effectively at frequencies around 50,-000 megacycles.

It is not only our technology that is dependent upon vacuum tubes. Fundamental scientific investigations would be sorely handicapped without them. Without vacuum tubes we would not have the powerful accelerators, the cyclotrons, synchrotrons, and linear accelerators, which physicists use in investigating the nature of the atomic nucleus. Neither would we have radiation detectors, amplifiers, and counters to observe nuclear reactions. Without vacuum tubes we would not have radio astronomy, which adds, to the knowledge which we obtain from the light of the stars, other and distinct information carried to us by the radio waves that the stars and the dust and gas scattered through the universe emit. Without vacuum tubes, biologists and physiologists would be deprived of delicate instruments—but there is almost no end to the uses of vacuum tubes, both in science and in industry.

The advance in the whole electronic art has followed advances in the vacuum tubes on which it has been based. As vacuum tubes of higher power have become available, as amplifiers with less noise have become available, as we have succeeded in making amplifiers which amplify higher frequencies, the electronic art has advanced to take advantage of these improved properties and ranges of operation. We have gone from radar using waves of several meters' length, which give broad beams and poor discrimination of angle, to 10- and 3-centimeter-wavelength radars with narrower beams and, so to speak, acuter vision, and finally for some purposes to millimeter-wave radars with needle-sharp beams. We have gone from early radio-telegraph signals of thousands of meters' wavelength to short-wave radio signals of ten to twenty meters' wavelength, which span the world carrying both code and voice, though sometimes with much static and distortion. We have gone further, to signals of 7.5 centimeters' wavelength sent across the country in hops between relay stations thirty miles apart and to signals of 5 centimeters' wavelength sent from continent to continent via communication satellites. All these advances could be made only when vacuum tubes with new capabilities became available.

Vacuum tubes do marvelous things. They offer us almost unlimited amplification. But they have inherent limitations as well. The usable gain is limited by noise. Most vacuum tubes will amplify a limited range or band of frequencies only. While the frequency of operation of vacuum tubes is continually pushed up (so some vacuum tubes have been made to amplify waves whose wavelength is only a quarter of an inch and whose frequency is 50,000,000,000 cycles per second) there are certain inherent limitations which make it difficult to design satisfactory vacuum tubes for extremely high frequencies. To understand the inherent limitations of vacuum tubes is to understand the limitations of the whole electronic art, for the limitations of amplifiers limit what we can do electronically.

Operation of the Triode

We cannot understand the limitations of vacuum tubes without understanding how they operate. Here, it is best to start with the very first of the vacuum tube amplifiers, the one Lee de Forest invented in the first decade of this century and called the *audion*. We now call it the *triode*.

The triode has numerous close relatives, such as the *tetrode*, *pentode*, and others. This family constitutes by far the most versatile of vacuum tubes. These are the tubes of your radio or TV receiver. Over a wide range of frequencies they will do almost anything, and that is about what they are called on to do.

Fig. 71 shows schematically the parts of a triode. These are an electron-emitting cathode (heated by an electric heater), a *grid* which is an array of fine parallel wires close to the cathode, and an anode to which the electrons from the cathode flow. All these electrodes are enclosed, of course, in a glass or metal *envelope* which is evacuated to a high degree.

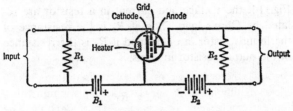

Figure 71

In operation, the anode is held positive with respect to the cathode, by means of a battery B_2 or another sort of electric source. The anode produces an electric field which tends to draw electrons in it from the cathode, just as in the diode described in Chapter Three.

The grid, however, is held negative with respect to the cathode by battery B_1, or by some other electric source. Thus, the grid produces an electric field which tends to keep electrons from leaving the cathode. When we make the grid less negative, the electron flow to the anode increases. When we make the grid more negative, the electron flow to the anode decreases.

For an amplifier we are interested not in the steady part of the anode current, but in the fluctuating current produced by the signal voltage applied across the input resistor R_1. The operation of a triode in amplifying signals is characterized by a constant g_m, different for different tubes, called the *transconductance*. If the signal voltage at the input in Fig. 71 is V_1, then the signal current I_2 which flows from the anode through the output resistor R_2 will be

$$I_2 = g_m V_1$$

As we noted in Chapter Three in connection with Fig. 14, the voltage and current in a resistor are related by Ohm's law. Thus, if R_1 is the resistance of the input resistor in ohms, and if R_2 is the resistance of the output resistor in ohms,

$$I_1 = \frac{V_1}{R_1}$$

$$V_2 = I_2 R_2 = g_m V_1 R_2$$

The input power P_1 is

$$P_1 = I_1 V_1 = \frac{V_1^2}{R_1}$$

The output power P_2 is

$$P_2 = I_2 V_2 = g_m^2 V_1^2 R_2$$

The power gain is the ratio of the input power to the output power:

$$\text{Power Gain} = g_m^2 R_1 R_2$$

Thus, increasing the transconductance g_m, or the input resistance R_1, or the output resistance R_2 will increase the gain.

This description of the operation of the triode is a little inaccurate because it disregards the effect of the anode potential on the current flow. Because the grid is closer to the cathode than the anode is, and because the effect of the anode in producing a field at the cathode is reduced by the presence of the grid, the grid has a much more powerful effect in controlling the current of electrons than the anode does—by a factor of 10 to 100. Nonetheless, if we make R_2 large enough, the power gain will be less than given by the above equation.

The Pentode

Effective as they are, today triodes are used in amplifiers only in rather special circumstances. A better tube, the *pentode*, has been invented. We have seen that in the triode variation in the anode voltage affects the electron flow in such a way as to reduce gain. Much worse, at high frequencies the electric field between the plate and the grid causes a displacement current to flow from the output (anode) to the input (grid) of the amplifier. This adversely affects the performance of the amplifier and may cause it to oscillate.

In the pentode of Fig. 72 a *screen grid*, g_2, is placed between the *control grid*, g_1, and the anode. This screen grid is held positive by battery B_2; it acts to draw electrons from the cathode no matter what the voltage of the anode may be. As in the case of the

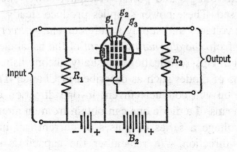

Figure 72

electron gun, most of the electrons which reach g_2 pass right through it; in this case they go to the anode.

A *suppressor grid*, g_3, is put between the screen grid, g_2, and the anode. This is a very open grid and is connected to the cathode, so that it is negative with respect to the anode. When electrons strike an electrode, *secondary electrons* are knocked out. When the anode is negative with respect to the screen grid, g_2, these secondary electrons would leave the anode and go to the screen were it not for the field produced near the anode by the suppressor grid, g_3.

Pentodes give higher gains than triodes, and they are easier to use in circuits because little displacement current flows from the anode back to the grid. Most of the tubes in your radio or TV set are pentodes. The tubes which supply several watts of audio power to the speaker will be pentodes.

An actual amplifier in a radio or TV set or in a microwave radio relay is, of course, more complicated than the simple circuit shown in Fig. 72. In that figure, for instance, batteries supply the required voltages and power. Actually, *power supplies* are used. These power supplies produce steady, constant voltages and supply steady currents—*direct current*—from the *alternating current* of the usual electric supply. This rectification is usually accomplished by means of diodes such as described in Chapter Three. A diode will conduct current in one direction only. By means of a diode one can obtain from an alternating voltage a series of pulses of current, all in the same direction. We remember the capacitors store electric charge, and that electric current tends to persist at a constant value in inductors. If, as shown in Fig. 73, the current from the diode is passed through a network made up of capacitors, C, and inductors,

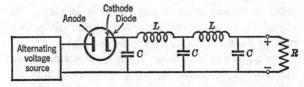

Figure 73

L, the pulsating current from the diode can be so stored and smoothed as to flow steadily and constantly through the resistance, R, for instance, or into an amplifier.

Too, in an actual amplifier the circuits will certainly not be merely a resistor, as shown in Figs. 71 and 72. In an intermediate frequency amplifier in a superheterodyne receiver, for instance, the circuit interconnecting two pentodes will probably be a double-tuned circuit, such as we discussed in Chapter Seven. Such a circuit coupling the anode of one pentode to the control grid of another is shown in Fig. 74.

The function of the resistor R_2 is to control the

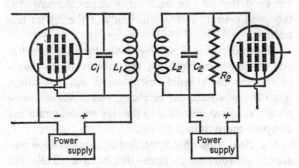

Figure 74

bandwidth of the amplifier, that is, to how wide a band of frequencies the amplifier will amplify. The higher R_2 is made, the greater the gain will be *but* making R_2 larger decreases the bandwidth.

For a given gain, making C_1 and C_2 larger decreases the bandwidth. Thus, in broad band amplifiers C_1 and C_2 are usually merely the unavoidable capacitances of the anode and the control grid to the other elements of the tube.

The bandwidth that pentodes can amplify is inherently limited, although bandwidths of several hundred megacycles can be attained at low gains.

Triodes and pentodes have another inherent limitation which hinges on size. When a triode or a pentode is operated at very high frequencies an appreciable part of a cycle of variation of the electric fields within the tube may take place during the passage of electrons from the cathode past the control grid of the tube. This can interfere with the effective operation of the tube. If we want to avoid such an effect, we have merely to halve the size of the tube each time we double the frequency of operation. Then, if we keep the current and the voltage constant, the tube will operate just as efficiently at the higher frequency.

This procedure of scaling down the tube size has one obvious disadvantage; the tube tends to disappear! One can't build microscopic vacuum tubes. Even if one could, the tiny cathodes could not supply the required current and the tiny anodes could not dissipate the required power.

A typical triode for operation at a microwave frequency of 4000 megacycles—that is, at a wavelength of 7.5 centimeters, or 3 inches—will have a grid consisting of 1000 wires per inch, each wire about $\frac{1}{8}$ of a thousandth of an inch in diameter. This is about a tenth the diameter of a human hair. The grid will be about $\frac{1}{2}$ a thousandth of an inch from the cathode, which is a flat disk about $\frac{3}{16}$ inches in diameter.

Such a tube is an effective microwave amplifier in a microwave radio-relay system. It will give about a watt of power. Since large antennas are used in such a system, the tube can send a television signal 20 to 40 miles. This, however, is about as well as we can do with triodes. Fortunately, there are other types of microwave tubes which can deliver kilowatts of power continuously and megawatts of power in pulses at microwave frequencies.

The Klystron and Rhumbatron

Back in the late 1930s the Varian brothers startled the world of electronics with a wonderful new microwave amplifier and oscillator called the *klystron*. Two things were involved in the klystron: a new way of acting on and controlling the electron flow and a new electrical circuit for producing the electric fields to act on the electron flow. The circuit, which the Varians called a *rhumbatron* and which we know as a microwave resonator, has already been pictured in Fig. 58 and described in the accompanying text.

Fig. 75 shows a klystron amplifier using two resonators. An electron gun produces an electron beam which is shot through the input resonator; the beam travels on for a distance, then passes through the output resonator, finally to be collected on a collector electrode. Often, as we noted in Chapter Four, a strong uniform magnetic field in the direction of the electron beam is used to assure that the electrons travel in nearly straight paths. Otherwise the electric fields produced by the electrons would cause the beam to widen as it traveled.

In the operation of the klystron of Fig. 75 an input signal traveling to the input resonator through a

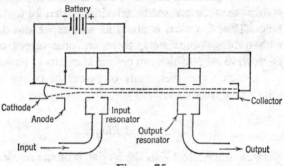

Figure 75

waveguide sets up electric and magnetic fields in the input resonator. As the electric field across the gap of the input resonator varies sinusoidally with time, changing from a negative field (a field in one direction) to a positive field (a field in the opposite direction) and back again repeatedly, it alternately slows down and speeds up the electrons passing through the resonator. While the electrons travel between the input resonator and the output resonator, the slowed-down electrons are overtaken by electrons which left later but which were speeded up by the varying electric field. Thus, the even flow of electrons entering the input resonator becomes bunched following the action of the input resonator in speeding up and slowing down (*velocity modulating*) the electrons of the electron stream.

The bunched electron stream constitutes a fluctuating current of electrons, an alternating current, whose frequency is the same as the frequency of the input signal. When this current flows across the gap of the output resonator, it sets up a strong electromagnetic oscillation inside the output resonator. Power leaks out of the output resonator through an aperture into the output waveguide, constituting an output signal considerably stronger than the input signal supplied to the input waveguide.

The Advantages of the Klystron Amplifier

What is the advantage of the klystron over the triode or pentode? Chiefly, it is that for a given frequency of operation the klystron is bigger. This is very important, because triodes for microwave frequencies are so small that they are hard to build, so small that they cannot be operated at high powers. A microwave klystron may be four feet long and may give a peak power of 30 million watts.

But how is it that the klystron can be so much larger than the triode? In the triode the signal acts on the electrons near the cathode, where the electrons are moving very slowly. Yet the electrons must get past the grid and to the anode in a fraction of a cycle of the amplified signal. This means that, in the microwave triode, the cathode, grid, and anode must be put very close together.

In the klystron the electrons are acted on by the input resonator after they have been accelerated to from one twentieth to one half the speed of light. Thus, they can travel much farther in a fraction of a cycle of change of field. The length of the field across the gap of the input resonator can be far, far greater than the cathode-to-grid spacing in a microwave triode, and still the electrons can traverse this field in a small part of a cycle, in a time which—for instance, at a frequency of 3,000,000,000 cycles per second (a wavelength of 10 centimeters, or 4 inches)—must be small compared with a third of a billionth of a second.

Klystron amplifiers have been made for a wide range of wavelengths, from perhaps 50 centimeters to around 1 centimeter, and for a wide range of powers, from a few watts up to peak powers of tens of megawatts. Klystrons delivering 15 kilowatts at frequencies ranging from 500 to 800 megacycles have been built to serve as amplifiers in ultra-high-frequency television transmitters. It is klystrons which supplied the powerful signals which were bounced off Venus and Mars in measuring their distances by radar.

Klystrons overcome many of the limitations of triodes. It is not too much to say that a whole microwave art could be based on klystrons alone, an art comparable to the lower-frequency art which has been based on triodes, tetrodes and pentodes.

While klystron amplifiers function effectively at higher frequencies than do triodes, both klystrons and triodes suffer from a particular inherent defect. Resonant circuits or resonators must be used with both types of tubes. The frequency of operation can be changed by adjusting or tuning these resonators or resonant circuits, but a broad band of frequencies cannot be amplified simultaneously by such tubes. Since the war this limitation on bandwidth has been overcome in a newer type of tube called a traveling-wave tube.

The Traveling-Wave Tube

Besides its intellectual interest and its social importance, there is a good deal of personal glamour connected with science, although I have tried to keep away from it in this book. About the origin of the traveling-wave tube, I will say only that it was invented in England in World War II by an Austrian architect, Rudolph Kompfner, who had always wanted to be a physicist. He had an opportunity to improve his knowledge of physics during his internment in the early part of the war. Released from internment, he worked on microwave tubes for the Admiralty. After the war he received a doctor's degree in physics from Oxford. Now he is in this country. In fact, he has been closely associated with me, not only in work on traveling-wave tubes, but in work on communication satellites as well.

Perhaps it took the fresh view of a man from another field of work to remove the bandwidth limitation of amplifiers. Kompfner did this simply by building an effective amplifier with no resonant circuit.

In an ordinary amplifier, the resonant circuit plays the very important part of allowing a small input power to produce a large electric field to control the electron flow. But in accomplishing this the band of frequencies that can be amplified is limited. We can liken the behavior of a resonator to that of a heavy pendulum swinging with little friction. By pushing the pendulum slightly each time it swings by, we can make it oscillate with a large amplitude even if we push lightly and supply very little power. It is very hard to make it swing at any other rate, however. To move it back and forth at any other frequency than its natural frequency of oscillation requires very strong pushes indeed. Such a pendulum with little friction is like an electrical resonant circuit with a high resistance. It is hard to produce a high voltage and electric field in such a circuit at any frequency very far removed from the resonant frequency.

If the electric field produced by the input signal is not to be made large by use of a high-resistance, narrow-band resonator, some other means must be found for the input signal to produce a strong effect on the electrons of an electron beam. Kompfner solved this problem by using a traveling wave to influence the electrons. He produced a wave with an electric field in the direction of motion of the electrons. He arranged matters so that the wave traveled with the same speed as the electrons in the electron beam. For instance, 1500-volt electrons (electrons accelerated by 1500 volts) travel with one thirteenth the speed of light. Using such electrons, Kompfner would provide a circuit around the beam which could guide an electromagnetic wave along the electron stream with one thirteenth the speed of light and he would apply the input power to this circuit. Thus, an electron which entered the circuit when the field was accelerating would continue to be in an accelerating field as both the electron and the wave traveled along, and an electron which entered the circuit when the field was retarding would continue to find itself in a retarding field.

This will be made clearer in examining the actual structure of a traveling-wave tube, as shown in Fig.

76. To the left we see an electron gun consisting of a cathode and an anode. To the far right is a collector

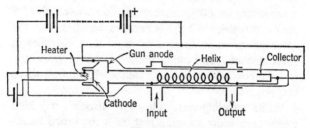

Figure 76

to collect the spent electrons. A longitudinal magnetic field, not shown, confines the electron flow to a narrow beam, as explained in Chapter Four. In between, the electrons travel through a *helix*—that is, a long coil of wire like a stretched door spring. All these parts are enclosed in an evacuated glass envelope.

It is the helix which carries the slow electromagnetic wave. As we noted in Chapter Seven an electromagnetic wave tends to follow the wire of the helix with about the speed of light. Thus, if the wire which is wound up to form the helix is about thirteen times as long as the helix it forms, the wave will travel along the length of the helix with about one thirteenth the speed of light. An input waveguide at the left end of the helix launches the wave, and the wave flows away from the right end of the helix into an output waveguide.

Kompfner showed mathematically, and found experimentally, that the strong cumulative influence of the electric field of the traveling electromagnetic wave does more than strongly bunch the electrons of the electron stream. The bunched electrons act to increase the amplitude of the electromagnetic wave. In fact, in a typical traveling-wave tube for operation at a frequency of 6000 megacycles (a wavelength of 5 cm), for which the helix is perhaps 5 inches long, the wave power may increase by more than 10 times in each inch of travel along the helix. Single traveling-wave tubes have given as much as 1,000,000 times power gain.

While traveling-wave tubes give astonishingly high gains, their most amazing feature is the broad bandwidth over which they amplify signals. The helix will carry waves over an extremely broad band of frequencies. Traveling-wave tubes have been made which amplify frequencies over a five-to-one range, and which amplify bands of frequencies several thousands of megacycles wide. In principle, such bandwidths could be used to carry tremendous numbers of telephone and television channels. So far, they have not been used for this purpose.

Uses of the Traveling-Wave Tube

Perhaps traveling-wave tubes have outstripped the needs of the communication art, or perhaps they have outstripped other aspects of the art. But they do have great virtues which have given them wide usage.

Because they have no sharply tuned resonators, traveling-wave tubes have proved remarkably stable in operation. They do not have to be readjusted, even occasionally.

The structures of traveling-wave tubes and of the magnets and electromagnetic circuits that go with them are remarkably simple and strong. Traveling-wave tubes can withstand the shock of being launched in missiles and satellites.

Traveling-wave tubes are quite efficient.

Low power traveling-wave tubes (up to powers of a few watts, at least) can be made to have a life of many years.

By using circuits different from the helix (in essence, a sequence of coupled resonators), traveling-wave tubes can be made to produce steady powers of several kilowatts or pulsed powers of several megawatts.

For these reasons, traveling-wave tubes have come to have a wide use in microwave radio relay systems here and abroad. The *only* vacuum tube in the Telstar communication satellite is a traveling-wave tube which produces the 2.5 watt signal that sends TV or telephone conversations to the far side of the ocean. And the 3 kilowatt signal that is sent from the ground station toward the satellite is produced by a traveling-wave tube.

Beyond all these things, traveling-wave tubes have also proved useful in a forefront of the microwave art, that of millimeter waves, or waves whose wavelengths are less than 1 centimeter (10 millimeters, 0.4 inches) and whose frequencies are correspondingly higher than 30,000 megacycles.

It is obvious that the range of frequencies encompassed by the wavelengths between 5 millimeters and 10 millimeters is as great as that of all longer waves. The entire broadcast and short-wave-radio ranges comprise a bandwidth of 30 megacycles. The wavelength range between 1 centimeter and .999 centimeters spans a frequency range of 30 megacycles. Millimeter waves offer bandwidth in almost inexhaustible quantities. We may expect that the almost unlimited resource of bandwidth provided by millimeter waves will become increasingly important as communication expands, and especially as television finds new group-to-group and perhaps person-to-person uses.

The traveling-wave tube, together with many related wave devices which have not been discussed here, seems to me to be a sort of glorious culmination of research and development in the field of vacuum tubes. What comes next?

Future Research and Development

The future clearly lies with amplifiers which depend on some phenomenon of quantum mechanics for their operation. These include the transistor, which is especially effective at frequencies lower than microwave frequencies, and the Esaki diode or tunnel diode, the parametric amplifier and the maser in the microwave and millimeter range of frequencies. Further, the laser or optical maser, which produces and amplifies coherent, narrow-band light signals—analogous to the radio waves produced by a radio transmitter rather than to the chaotic, noisy, broad-band power produced by the sun or by a light bulb—has opened up the possibility of extending all the techniques of radio communication to communication by the extremely high-frequency electromagnetic waves of light.

Vacuum tubes are still very important and will continue to be so. They are still our only means for amplifying radio signals of very high powers. But research has turned to other fields. At the Bell Telephone Laboratories, where I have worked, the people who used to do research on traveling-wave tubes and related devices have now turned to masers and lasers. But the experience they had with vacuum tubes has stood them in good stead. They are still dealing with waves and resonators and Maxwell's equations. In fact, everything in this book is knowledge that is needful to some aspect of this new work. But the phenomena of quantum mechanics, which are beyond the scope of this volume, have been added to open up new and exciting possibilities.

APPENDIX

Remarks on the M.K.S. (meter-kilogram-second) system of measurement and on the equations in this book.

The equations in this book have been written so that they hold true using M.K.S. units. In this system of units, length is measured in meters, mass in kilograms, and time in seconds. The following discussion goes a little beyond questions raised in the various chapters, but the additional material may be of interest to technically-inclined readers.

1 meter $= 3.281$ feet; 1 foot $= .3048$ meters
1 kilometer $= 1000$ meters
1 meter $= 100$ centimeters
1 centimeter $= 10$ millimeters
1 meter $= 10^{10}$ Angstrom units (abbreviated Å)
1 meter $= 10^6$ microns

All physical quantities have descriptive names called *dimensions*. A mass may be 30 kilograms. Here *kilogram* is the name or dimension associated with mass. Velocity, for instance, is measured in meters per second. When we give the magnitude of a particular velocity, v, as 100 meters per second we write

$$v = 100 \frac{(\text{meter})}{(\text{second})}$$

It is the practice to use the singular (*meter*) instead of the plural (*meters*) to avoid confusion in the case of more complicated quantities to be discussed later.

The kilogram is a unit of mass; that is, of quantity of matter, not of force.

1 kilogram = 2.205 pounds; 1 pound = .4536 kilograms

1 kilogram = 1000 grams

The unit of force used in the equation

$$f = ma \text{ newton}$$

is the *newton*.

Gravitational attraction exerts a force on a mass. At the surface of the earth the acceleration of gravity is 9.81 meters per second per second; this is written

$$9.81 \frac{\text{(meter)}}{\text{(second)}^2}$$

$$\left(32.2 \frac{\text{(feet)}}{\text{(second)}^2} \right)$$

Thus, at the earth's surface, the force, f, of gravity acting on a mass of one kilogram is 9.81 newtons, and the acceleration of any falling mass is 9.81 meters per second per second.

Newton's law of gravitation may be written

$$f = \frac{Gm_1 m_2}{r^2} \text{ newton}$$

The gravitational constant, G, is

$$G = 6.67 \times 10^{-11} \frac{\text{(newton) (meter)}^2}{\text{(kilogram)}^2}$$

The M.K.S. unit of work or energy is the *joule*. A force of one newton pushing an object a distance of one meter does a work of one joule. The M.K.S. unit of power is the *watt*. When a work of one joule is done in one second, the power is one watt.

$$1 \text{ kilowatt} = 1000 \text{ watts}$$
$$1 \text{ kilowatt} = 1.34 \text{ horsepower}$$

Electrical power, P, in watts is given by the product of the current, I, in amperes and the voltage, V, in volts.

$$P = IV \text{ watt}$$

When a convection current of I amperes flows for 1 second, the electric charge transferred is 1 *coulomb*. The charge, q, of an electron is

$$q = -1.602 \times 10^{-19} \text{ coulomb}$$

The mass, m, of an electron is

$$m = 9.11 \times 10^{-31} \text{ kilogram}$$

Electric field, E, is measured in volts per meter. Electric flux, ϕ, is measured in coulombs (by Gauss's law, electric flux is directly related to charge). Magnetic intensity, H, is measured in amperes per meter, and magnetic flux, ψ, is measured in *webers*. The constants, ϵ and μ, used in relating ϕ to E and ψ to H are

$$\epsilon = 8.85 \times 10^{-14} \frac{(\text{coulomb})}{(\text{volt})(\text{meter})^2}$$

$$\mu = 1.257 \times 10^{-6} \frac{(\text{weber})}{(\text{ampere})(\text{meter})}$$

As we saw in Chapter Five, the velocity of light, c, is

$$c = \frac{1}{\sqrt{\mu\epsilon}} = 3 \times 10^8 \frac{(\text{meter})}{(\text{second})}$$

A capacitor which has a charge of Q coulombs when the voltage across it is V volts has a *capacitance*, C, measured in *farads*.

$$C = \frac{Q}{V} \text{ farad}$$

We see that the dimension *farad* is the same as (*coulomb*)/(*volt*).

The inductance of a coil is measured in henries. The dimension *henry* is the same as (*weber*)/(*meter*).

INDEX

Acceleration: defined, 31

Algebra: discussed, 12–15

AM: signals, 180–84

Ampere: measured, 60

Amplifiers: uses of, 195–96

Amplitude: defined, 100; wave pattern, 103

Amplitude modulation. See AM

Angular momentum: discussed, 44–46; defined, 44; conservation of, 44, 45; as vector, 44

Anode: described, 58–60

Antenna: described, 114–17; effective area, 117; discussed, 158–63

Array, 159

Band, 124. See also Channel

Bandwidth, 190–93, 204, 212–14 passim

Betatron, 137–38

Capacitance, 171

Capacitors, 169–73

Carrier system, 189–90

Cathode, 58–60

Cathode-ray oscilloscope. See Oscilloscope

Channel, 189–90

Charged particles, 50

Circular polarization. See Polarized waves

Coaxial-cable-carrier system, 189–90

Coaxial line, 162

Communication satellites: waves used in, 149; receivers in, 188; vacuum tubes, 197, 213

Component of velocity, 46–47

Concave mirrors, 111. See also Lenses

Consenser. See Capacitors

Condenser lens, 91

Condenser microphone, 171

Conductors, 56–58, 62, 72, 153–54, 160, 161–62

Conservation of energy, law of, 46–49

Constants, 33–34, 130–31, 155–57

Control grid. See Pentode

Convection current, 135, 144

Converging lens, 84

Current: radiation from, 143–46

Current flow, 60, 73, 76. See also Diode

Cycle: defined, 96–97

electrons and waves

Here is the first paperback edition of a classic introduction to the art and science of electronics, fully revised and updated by the author, John R. Pierce. For the general reader and the student, Dr. Pierce begins with an illuminating examination of the laws of physics that govern the motion of particles and waves. The author goes on to discuss "Maxwell's Wonderful Equations," which describe the behavior of electrons in electrical and magnetic fields. Then Dr. Pierce explains transformers, vacuum-tube amplifiers, traveling-wave tubes, and the transistors—all instruments basic to the art of generating, transmitting, and receiving signals and messages.

In his work at the Bell Telephone Laboratories as Executive Director of the Research-Communications Principles and Systems Divisions, Dr. Pierce played an important role in the development of Project Echo, the forerunner of Telstar. Dr. Pierce was awarded a 1963 National Medal of Science. He is a member of the National Academy of Sciences and a Fellow of the American Academy of Arts and Sciences.

The Science Study Series is part of a dramatic new program for the teaching and study of physics, originated recently by distinguished American scientists and educators meeting at the Massachusetts Institute of Technology. This series of up-to-date, authoritative, and readable science books is prepared under the direction of the Physical Science Study Committee of Educational Services Incorporated, and is published in co-operation with Doubleday-Anchor Books.

A DOUBLEDAY ANCHOR BOOK